Theoretical Approaches
in
Dance-Movement Therapy
Volume II

Edited by

Penny Lewis Bernstein, Ph.D, ADTR

KↃH

KENDALL/HUNT PUBLISHING COMPANY
Dubuque, Iowa

About the cover

The evolutionary three figure sculpture was created by a woman who was in Jungian Depth Movement Therapy with the editor. Her journey toward the individuation of her own embodied feminine ego is conceptualized in Chapter 2, "Object Relations Theory Within a Jungian Perspective" in the discussion of the ontogeny of feminine ego consciousness.

B   403463   01

Contents

Preface

Since the initial publication of Eight
Theoretical Approaches In Dance-Movement
Therapy, the field has continued to expand.
Section I adds four more frames of reference
for consideration. Recognition of Blance Evan
as one of the founders of the field of dance
therapy with neurotics has brought her work
to the forefront and broadened the roots
available to tap. Iris Rifkin-Gainer along
with Bonnie Bernstein and Barbara Melson have
drawn from their years of training with
Blanche Evan as well as from primary source
material to present an accurate account of
Evan's theory and practice.

Chapter two looks at object relations
theory and its effect on depth analysis
within Freudian, neoFreudian, and Jungian
frames of reference. Much of what is
foundational in dance-movement therapy
parallels the etiological orientation and
conceptual premises of the therapeutic
process. Penny Bernstein provides an
understanding of the use of Laban/Kestenberg
movement profiling. Employing the theories of
Mahler and Winnicott, a mode of object
relational movement assessment is provided.
Arlene Avstreih follows with clinical
grounding as she demonstrates the application
of a psychoanalytic movement therapy approach
in a case study. Bernstein then explores a
Jungian view of the self and the development
of ego consciousness in both men and women
through assessment of symbolic movement
themes in authentic movement and other modes
of active imagination. Finally, she grounds

her material with a Jungian dance therapy
case study.

A systems approach to family therapy has
become a vitally important vehicle in
psychotherapy. The work of Judith Bell in the
use of dance therapy has served to expand the
field into this orientation. "Family Therapy
in Motion" is the first depth work of its
kind. The basic premises of the interpersonal
dimensions in the family are delineated in
detail. Dance therapy techniques for family
assessment are outlined. Phase-related issues
in the family therapy process along with the
corresonding role of the movement therapist
are described and grounded in clinical
material.

Erma Dosamantes-Alperson's "Experiential
Movement Psychotherapy" draws upon a
Rogerian phenomenological base and has been
influenced by the widespread use of imaging
toward intrapsychic transformation. Her
interface of enactive, image and lexical
experiential modalities provide a powerful
vehicle through which the individual can
retrieve unconscious material toward
awareness and individuation. The efficacy of
this approach has been validated in one of
the few statistically sound outcome studies
extant in the field.

Section II continues the research into
dance-movement therapy therapeutic process.
As in Eight Theoretical Approaches in Dance-
Movement Therapy, the phenomenological method
has been employed. The research extends into
a depth exploration of the phenomena of the
somatic unconscious. A sample population of
dance-movement therapists were selected whose
theoretical orientations, training, and
clinical work span those extant in the field.
The relationship of the explicated phenomena

to the experience of feminine archetypes
within the collective unconscious is
discussed toward a more androgenous approach
to therapy.

The final chapter delves more deeply
into the use of the phenomenon of the somatic
unconscious in the transference-
countertransference relationship between the
patient(s) and movement therapist. This
invisible inner pas de deux provides one of
the most powerful forums for transformation
of childhood wounds and the constellation of
the numinous toward individuated
consciousness.

Acknowledgments

To those who ponder meaning and seek the
answers, the editor of this book continues to
be indebted. For these individuals have
facilitated the ever emerging relationship to
the wisdom of that which transforms in dance-
movement therapy. The contributors'
willingness to engage in the labor of the
dance of experience and ideas has brought
forth volume II. Thank you all.

The cover photograph of the sculpture as
well as other patient productions were taken
by Douglas Gilbert.

Finaly, the supportive critiquing and
rich gnosis of analysts Donald Kalsched,
Nathan Schwartz-Salant, and Sylvia Perera has
helped birth Section II. My deepest gratitude
as I continue to learn from my soma about
depth movement therapy.

Penny Lewis Bernstein

Section I

Theoretical Frames
of Reference

Chapter 1

Dance/Movement/Word Therapy: The Methods of Blanche Evan

By: Iris Rifkin-Gainer, M.A., ADTR*
with Bonnie Bernstein, M.Ed., ADTR**
and Barbara Melson, M.S., ADTR***

Genesis

My early childhood memories of creative dance classes date back to 1947. My teacher, Blanche Evan, was a small, graceful and delightful woman often clad in long flowing clothes. She played percussion on a marvelous selection of instruments collected world wide, and drew from recordings of every

---

*Iris Rifkin-Gainer is an Adjunct Assistant Professor on the faculty of N.Y.U.'s Graduate Dance Therapy Program. She studied with Blanche Evan from 1947 to 1982 and is a former Director of the Blanche Evan Dance Therapy Centre; she also has a Dance Therapy practice with adults. The Genesis section has been written by Ms. Rifkin-Gainer.
**Bonnie Bernstein is a Dance/Movement Therapist in private practice in the Bay area. She trained with Blanche Evan from 1970 to 1982. She has also worked as a supervisor, geriatric consultant, researcher on therapeutic dance of West Africa and Malaysia, and is an Adjunct Professor at Long Island University.
***Barbara Melson is a Dance Therapist at Gracie Square Hospital in N.Y.C. She trained with Blanche Evan from 1973 to 1982. She is also a Dance Therapist in private practice, a teacher of creative dance and guest lecturer at Hunter College.

possible type of music for our weekly
classes. At times we leapt and spun across
the room to the beat of the drum, while on
other occasions we curled up tenderly in
silence. To me, it was quite natural to
particpate in these well structured classes,
disciplined yet free. Each Saturday we
experienced a directed warm-up with some
carefully chosen technical exercise on our
own level. This was followed by exhilerating
rhythmic locomotion and improvisation to
themes and images that spanned the inner
worlds of our feelings and imaginations as
well as the external life around us.

The clarity and soundness of Evan's work
with children as individual human beings
provided the groundwork for her dance therapy
with the client population she came to refer
to as the "normal neurotic urban adult." Her
devotion to the art of dance and her
continuing involvement in creative dance as a
source of and route to self-expression were
the cornerstones of her choreography, her
teaching and her work as a dance therapist.

Evan volunteered at Bellevue Hospital in
the children's ward during World War II, but
most of her work as a teacher and a dance
therapist took place in her own private
studios. There was an organic evolution from
the creative dance work which emphasized "the
physical equivalent of the psyche in the body
through action" (Evan, 1948, p. 4) and
invited personal expression, into dance
therapy which used those expressions to
understand and to change what had become
habitual, "stuck" and neurotic. Evan first
referred to her work as "dance therapy" in
1958, the year of her lecture demonstration
"The Psychological Content of Children's
Dance."

4

In this chapter, we have attempted to use Evan's words whenever possible, drawing from over ten years of personal communications and from her teachings.

Theoretical Model

Concepts

View of the Individual
The Moving Being

"The human body functions only by movement: the inner moving processes of muscles, joints, nerves, glands, and the five senses live by movement. Mentality and spirituality derive from a body in motion internally and of necessity externally. Adler said this succinctly:

" 'We can ascertain then in the very beginning that the development of the psychic life is connected with movement, and that the evolution and progress of all those things which are accomplished by the soul are conditioned by the free movability of the organism. This movability stimulates, promotes, and requires an always greater intensification of the psychic life. Imagine an individual to whom we have predicted every movement, and we can conceive of his psychic life as at a standstill.

"There is a strict corollary between movement and psychic life. In the evolution of the psychic life, therefore, we must consider everything which is connected with movement. We see that both mind and body are expressions of life: they are parts of the whole of life. And we begin to understand their reciprocal relations in that whole. The

5

life of man is the life of a moving being.' "
(Evan, 1970).

Individual as Unique

Blanche Evan herself was very much of an
individual in her lifestyle and in her
involvement as an artist. This both
influenced and was reflected in her way of
viewing the individual in therapy.

The uniqueness of the individual was
always a major focus in Evan's work. She
believed both in the basic integrity of the
human being at birth and in the potential for
change. She saw the individual as a sum total
of his/her own personal, familial and social
history, as reflected in the use and dis-use
of developmentally determined body structure.
A therapy goal, basic to her philosophy was
movement toward individual autonomy. She
believed that each person is ultimately alone
and through dance therapy can arrive at the
ability to "stand on one's own two feet,"
able to depend on the self in this
"container," the body. A major task in Dance
Therapy is to answer the question "Who am
I?", often asked by clients. Evan once stated
that when clients first ask the question,
"they aren't yet." In therapy, through the
activation of the will, they begin to become
able to define what they really want and what
their values are so that they can make
choices from their own perspective rather
than others'. Through employment of conscious
will they can begin to change what is
neurotic or what they don't want to retain,
while gaining an orientation to the reality
of the body, accepting limitations, and
building on strengths where they already
exist, be they evident or buried.

6

Individual Development within the Social Situation

Evan believed that most individuals are born healthy with a potential for growth and expansion, taking into account the original physical limits of the body. She had a deep respect for and awe of the infant and the young child. She believed that it was possible for her adult clients to find some equivalent of that "born health" as inspiration and image, in their movement range and reclaimed sponteneous joy of movement. The integrity, the totality of the infant, expressing, moving, communicating, are models for her dance therapy work. The "socializing" which begins very early, the "do's and don'ts, shoulds and shouldn'ts" influence the child, and his/her choices. These choices, e.g., to avoid angering a parent, to accommodate an elder, and to placate; make their mark on the body appearing later as inhibition, tension, resistance, apathy, deadness and overcontraction. She also pointed to the over-reaction against this socializtion and loss of uniqueness in the self-indulgent adult who resents any demands and restrictions. Evan saw both the exaggeration of inhibitions and the overemphasis on self-indulgence as reactions to the Western-industrialized-child-centered-middle-class-family. Wherever appropriate she addressed these elements in her work through the introduction of material from other cultures where the folk and ethnic dances emphasized moving together and being part of the group.

As the young child begins to develop, he or she has an intrinsic need for the family and society (discussed at length in Evan's The Child's World [1948]). The child seems to have a need to relate to the world and for

7

the world to relate to him/her within the child's own scale and scope. Her respect for and utilization of dance and music elements from non-industrialized cultures is consistent with Evan's <u>disrespect</u> for the kinds of impingements on natural development which threaten innate individuality in our culture, without providing the benefits of true socialization in a supportive community.

In her work both in creative dance with normal children and in dance therapy for the "normal neurotic urban adult," Evan believed in the importance of age specific actions occurring in the normal development of the young child. Grasping, dropping, throwing, running, falling, standing, moving through space, skipping exuberantly, galloping, and rolling are just a few examples. In dance therapy the attitudes of family members and important others with regards to these actions may need to be identified and re-enacted to free the body of the prevalent "no" often experienced in childhood. Feared danger, noise, disruption of adult activities, associations with personal bodily behaviors considered unacceptable by adults may engender negative responses from the parent. Often, later, in the child-become-adult's view and use of the body, these restrictions are experienced as habitual tensions, blocks and limits in range of movement.

Evan emphasized the utilization of movements which a particular client did <u>not</u> do at the appropriate age because of restrictions or did do, but "lost." She believed that some reparative process could go on in the physicalization of those earlier ages through the specific elements of movement and dance. The client can experience the body in rhythmical ways, with specific coordinations in uses of time and space. For example, the sequence of first galloping, then skipping may be done in the session by the adult with the acknowledged adult body, eventually recapturing some of the freedom and rhythmic quality of the child.

In summary, Evan viewed each individual client as a unique totality, but she also ascribed to one of Adler's "Basic Propositions of Individual Psychology: The individual cannot be considered apart from his social situation," (Ansbacher and Ansbacher, 1956, p. 2); nor, she would add, from that of his family.

Health and Neurosis

"I believe that most human beings are born normal; and normal to me means having the potential for growth, health and creativity. My work remembers this and it (this memory) needs constantly to become part of the consciousness of the client" (1977). Health to Evan meant psychophysical health uniquely tempered to each individual. She emphasized the necessity of identifying and changing tenacious habits, which were blatantly or subtly self-destructive. She was fascinated with the relationships between the phsysical, the psychophysical and the psychological.

Evan encouraged a client to deal with a problem from all sides, because she believed in the totality of the individual even when in disharmony with itself. So in a sense, every behavior was PSYCHO SOMATIC, AND PSYCHO PHYSICAL. In her later years, she drew her attention to researching the chemical imbalances within the body which result from and cause emotional disturbance.

9

Evan was often able to work with an individual and "track down" what she called "nests," physical manifestations of the neurosis. An example of such a nest in a typical "American urban neurotic client" can be found in the hands. "These people have apathy in the hands. A common cultural cause is that the hands in the city are extremely limited in their tasks, and emotional gesture is considered vulgar. Masturbation for the child is considered immoral by the parents. Under all, repression of hands goes way back into infancy in expression, natural evolution, use, and self assertion. In this person's therapy, what has been squelched must be revived; then the hand is integrated to the arm, the arm to the back and that to the totality" (Evan, 1980).

At other times she maintained an overview of a particular client and just kept simultaneously "chipping away" at many different aspects, through technical work, improvisation and re-enactment.

Evan believed specific dysfunctions, such as sexual dysfunction, were symptoms of the deeper and broader reaches of the neurosis. She did deal with sexualilty in her work, not from the point of view of dysfunction; but rather as it related to the individual's issues of self image, autonomy, letting go and holding on, giving and receiving, early male and female figures, intensity of body feeling (sensation), dynamic intensity and the limits of action. Ongoing questions for her included "How can you let go to movement if you cannot let go sexually?" (and vice versa.) She thought of sexuality as a basic element of health and this attitude was evident in her approach to physicality: developing resilient use of the knees, encouraging spontaneity and fullness of body action. She viewed much of this culture of "self-involvement", despite promiscuity, as turned inward; unable to truly share, or give and take; its normal neurotics limited or overly dramatic in their self expression.

Evan viewed the neurotic individual of our time within the neurotic culture of our time where the social neurosis is a tremendous influence and saw the particular neurotic effect of the "normal middle class" family on the individual. Although many normal neurotics do indeed function at work, school and in the family, their inner lives and most intimate relationships reflect the disturbance of the delicate balances among society, economy, family and an individual's body, mind and spirit.

In an article entitled "....The Least Movement of the Body" Evan (1970) writes:

> This is the machine age. Machine displaces human action. Formerly human work expended natural energy. Work demanded big and small muscle use. Work kept the blood circulating and increased the lung power. Work gave dignity and a reality to ego. These are only some of the ingredients that have now become a vacuum. (The hopeless urbanite replies "Just as well--what good to breathe in more polluted air." What a vicious cycle industrialization has sprawled.) Enormous and small machines and "make life easier" gadgets deprive the human body of action necessary to health. Finally the adult's inclination to "no effort" is exploited by amoral business and advertising: "no need for the body to work--keep fit without exercise--use the vibrating belt," etc. No need for

11

the person to DO, only to be done to.
Depersonalization.

In addition to the more physical
aspects, this replacement of work by the
machine has had far reaching PSYCHO-
LOGICAL EFFECTS, ON AFFECTS, unknown to
most therapists, even to those who refer
patients with the request "help them
release their tension and express their
anger." Physical work is a great outlet
for anger and aggression and their
accompanying tension, even when used
symbolically in an action class. Work
energy is a socially acceptable subli-
mation and displacement for these
feelings. To the private urban citizen,
to be civilized means to repress
aggression and anger with no active
alternate supplied. Yet the anger and
aggression are there. Adrenalin is
automatically produced in the body for
action which "normally" results from
these feelings. With action repressed,
the energy is diverted to different
kinds of tension: rigidity at one
extreme, apathy at the other. Every
dance therapist is familiar with both
psycho-physical states. The 'head' takes
over--how many of my referred patients
come to sessions with headaches; leave
without them; the brain wheels turn
round and round, ironically in a
machine-like way; the nerves work
overtime to KEEP THE BODY FROM ACTION;
hostilities store up until they come
near to bursting and the media and
professional sports take over offering a
sick outlet of passive violence--"read
all about it"--"see it on TV." The no-
outlet energy for some becomes active-
destructive violence, outwardly to the
world and/or inwardly to one's self.

12

Finally an enormous amount of
energy is used to maintain self-
defeating attitudes. The human body
loses its form, its grace, its power to
express, and finally the natural NEED to
express is stifled. ("I can't cry.")
Body and spirit split and begin to
atrophy; ego power shrinks to low self-
esteem with an ineptness for both anger
and love. In our dance therapy sessions
those who cannot be strong in movement
can neither be tender; those who cannot
express love can neither dance anger.
There may be millions of neurotics who
fit diagnostic cabinets but there are
also millions of a nondescript nature
who fit into the category of what the
new age has done to the human being.

Inaction and depression go hand in
hand. Bleuler described the "melancholic
triad consisting of depressive affect,
inhibition of action and inhibition of
thinking," Beck in Depression refers to
"...a reduction in spontaneous
activity."

Aridity of feeling is seen in the
frozen face of the neurotic. The mask
presents an acceptable face to the
world, a nothing non-commital
expressionless expression. When a
patient says "I don't feel anything" I
suggest: move and you may stir up
feelings.

Dance

"Dance is the one art that projects the
spirit of man through the body, the spirit
fused with the body of motion outward into
space and time (Evan, 1970).

"Very simply, may I say that my work as
a dance therapist derives from dance. Self
expression in dance equals transmutation into
emotion" (Evan, 1969, p. 1). Evan believed
totally in the dance and its components:
time, space, dynamics, body movement and
content, to achieve the ultimate human
expression. She employed these elements as
fully and specifically in her work as a dance
therapist as she did in the art of dance.
Although she appreciated and studied many
forms of dance, she held that an unstylized
technique which dealt sequentially with the
anatomical range of each portion of the body,
and of the body as a whole, provided the best
base for personal expressive dance, be it
dance as a performance art, creative dance or
dance therapy. Her brief two and a half years
of study with Bird Larson who died
prematurely in 1927 paved the way for the
development of her system of functional
technique.

Evan (1969) writes,

functional technique is the simple
designation for the system of technique
I have built through a long professional
career...a technique that respects
nature's plan of the body in action and
that also reckons with the effects of
our culture on the human body, so many
of them deleterious...changing the body
tonus from destructive tension to
resilience is vital.

In functional techique I start with
a person's body as it is and go very
progressively and slowly through any
state necessary to what the body needs.
My technique makes demands upon the body
in terms of self-discipline, but it is
neither static nor mannered. Because it

14

flows through the evanescent forms of
function, it does not impede individual
expressive dance. I include in the realm
of exercise the work on drums--for
rhythm, the study of the body surface
planes and space direction, the breaking
down of structural, habitual and
situational tensions as they affect the
body, and rehabilitation. The
acquirement of skill per se, is a result
but not a first objective. Total
experience precedes shape and form.

For instance, you develop the
strength in your feet in relation to
your personal structure. When you are
developing technique, you are not
expressing a style of movement, and when
you improvise, you don't have any form
to hold on to: that's very intentional.

The role of improvisation is to
find depth...D-E-P-T-H in feeling and
commensurate movement (1969, pp. 8-12).

Evan developed organically from a dancer
into a dance therapist, finding specific
application in her work for the lay student
and the neurotic client. She saw "neurotic
problems dragged into technique, getting in
the way of technical growth," and she seized
the opportunity to "separate muscular strain
from attitude" (1975). Technique in dance
therapy offered the possibility to
differentiate "between the use of muscles for
contraction and for expressive purposes;
between the body image and reality" (1979).

Emphasis on clarity of the body surface
planes (front, sides, back, diagonals)
essential in her technical dance work, gained
added importance for the neurotic client;
encouraging "ownership" of the body and the

15

ability to sense and use the body three-dimensionally. The client could reclaim "forgotten" body areas, and exert positive control over his/her own body.

In addition, functional technique in therapy is particularly suitable for individualization. It is "a system that helps you to find, confront and do something to correct weak muscles, self-destructive posture and nervous tension that inhibit free flowing muscular energy" (Evan, (1969).

Evan's interest in the origins of various tensions grew directly out of her work with the urban client. She distinguished structural tensions, resulting from stress placed on the body by irregularities, such as legs of differing lengths from habitual tensions, the chronic personal patterns of body carriage and use. She also dealt with situational tensions, arising from the demands of isolated encounters, e.g. an argument with one's boss, or activities, e.g. tennis, a difficult ballet class or rush hour driving.

Through the use of drums in therapy Evan emphasized the rhythmic possibilities of the expressive human being; both unifying the body in action and offering an effective channel for catharsis.

The truly creative, imaginative and transcendent aspects of dance join the discipline of an exhaustive technique, resulting in dance which is skilled, expressive, individual and human. Evan drew on dance and music from around the world as inspiration and education in the many facets and qualities of the human expressive experience. "Dance in therapy as I practice it helps to restore the client's acceptance of his own body as a total entity, with its imperfections and helps to inspire him and to teach him how to improve upon himself and how to sunder his rigidities" (1967, p. 1).

Therapy

Evan best states her beliefs about therapy in personal communications:

Therapy involves "insight for action-- not just insight. Therapy involves education" (1974). Adler has said that emotions can be educated, "psychophysical states can also be educated" (Melson, 1980).

"Therapy is communication, a two-way passage. It involves directness rather than circuitousness...there is not enough time!" (Evan, 1977).

"Therapy is work, hard work. Work is getting down to the specific. Generalities are not therapy. The generality is hiding the material; (it) is resistance. Generalization is not therapy. Unless therapy is direct, you are not counteracting what the client is used to, which is evasion, non-communication. Time wasted in therapy can be measured by the amount of generalization" (1978).

"Unless a session stirs up, it's useless. If you don't stir up, you stagnate" (1980).

"Pleasure in therapy is dangerous, pain is more appropriate."

"The work is not done in the session. The work is clarified in the session but only done in the outside world. The objective of increased health should deal with the reality of the 24 hour day that the client lives" (1980).

"Can therapy cure? Wounds never heal completely. A person's life is always going to reflect either having been healed or that it still has a 'sack of poison' in it" (1982). "Therapy is for a better life, on the client's terms. A basic objective: to assist the client toward becoming stronger (and to develop) the sense of self and the courage to be who/what he/she wants to be. Therapy with the neurotic client (moves) toward choice; (toward) the strength of the individual to keep pursuing the satisfaction that fits with the personality and character" (1980).

Dance Therapy

In the year before her death Blanche Evan began to refer to her work as "Dance: A Basic Therapy." She was concerned with the totality of the client; and in October of 1981, after musing into the early hours, she wrote the following note: "The Blanche Evan Methodologies of Creative Dance, Functional Technique and the Word in the use of therapy for the total person," adding, "too long, but this is the idea." Earlier, (1978) she had stated "Dance Therapy is not just to evoke or encourage feelings. It must deal with feelings beyond expression. In the first phase of therapy (one of the client's tasks is) to begin to feel. You work toward and on expressive action. Don't work on changing the client's feelings, (but on making the client's body more his/her body. An aim of dance therapy is to rekindle the initial life force that you had when you were born, (also) to keep it a creative therapy so that you are a participant of your own change, not an

18

observer. You are your own person; therapy
has to be an interchange. The therapist
helps, guides, listens, but you (the client)
are there to create change. This is an active
kind of therapy: to get back all you once
had, were. In dance therapy, the body is the
medium of the therapy itself. Dance therapy
is a process of exposure. The levels of dance
therapy are: first, to externalize, then
catharsis...movement and sound without
judgement, then to gain strength, resilience
and flexibility, to shape and remake your
life (1974).

"...the big thing is giving. How can the
client truly give herself to dance therapy
when she cannot give herself to love? Perhaps
the whole evolution of the (dance) therapy is
in reaching, giving and receiving. The person
needs to understand that the body is
expressing and the body is holding back. To
learn to feel again, feel meaningfully is the
aim of dance therapy" (1974).

In practice and training Evan was
concerned with "the recognition of the
necessity of the word and the continuous
exploration of its overuse which distracts
from the dance potential" (1982). Her
commitment was to dance therapy as a field in
itself and she continually searched for fresh
uses of the "word," as she called it, which
supported dance and movement work.

Theoretical Formulations

Method of Identification

In Evan's work, the individual's
changing sense of self is of great import.
Her belief that "body image should be moved
not talked" (1971) offers the possibility for

dialogue between subjective feelings, attitudes, and the reality orientation of body work. She might ask "Are your arms weak, or do your arms _feel_ weak?"

Evan was guided in her work by the functioning body, and the image of the body "as nature made it." The individual's mis-alignment, expressiveness, inhibition, and repression is viewed in relation to the client's affectual and attitudinal experience. This method involves viewing the totality of the person in action and "ferreting" out the discrepancies among the depth of feeling expressed, movement ability, verbal specificity, spontaneous expression, and creativity. These discrepancies are manifested in "what the client needs to express and the inadequacy of his or her psychophysicality" (1982). This "inadequacy" is apparent in the inhibition and distortion of posture and body action. She has stated, "my main interest is in knowing the body as nature made it, then as the student or client distorts it through neurosis or ignorance or lack of awareness" (1978). A way of moving or being in the body which appears to deviate from what "nature intended" is not in itself enough data for "diagnosis" but "the rate of growth (in the course of therapy) is a clue for the (degree of severity of the) client's neurosis and will to change" (1981).

Therapeutic Process

Movement from neurosis toward health for Evan meant making one's body one's own.

"The words which guide the therapy process are, as stated by Evan, 'honesty, concentration and work'...her work provides verbal directives for movement experiences

which stimulate and channel therapeutic
material and guide the client to work, to
feel, to find the source of nis/her problems,
to uncover his unconscious attitudes and
feelings and find new life action" (Melson,
1980, p. 22). Evan delineates this as
repersonalization or the reintegration of
body, mind and spirit (1973).

Basic to the therapeutic process
particular to dance therapy is "belief in the
client's body actually going through
physicalization of 24 hour day life action.
To see reality for what it is--physical
reality, objective reality, physicality is
primary" (1980). The client begins to "move
from egocentricity (self), out, to include
the world...from self, autonomy to other
(another), to world" (1978).

The therapeutic process is dynamic. Evan
states "Change apathy to volition and tension
to resiliency. Respect and utilize the
ingredients of the body as much as the
ingredients of memory, conscious behavior and
unconscious behavior. The first step is to
get the client to feel, then to use feelings
in expressive action. After a course of
"letting out", i.e. 'I accuse you', move
toward 'I let it happen': claiming one's
role. 'I chose it, I made it happen' "(1981)
(and "I can change it.")

Thus the therapeutic process results in
the client's acceptance of his/her body as a
total entity and in his/her capacity for
"action for life change" (1981).

Role of the Dance Therapist

The dance therapist must "reorient
herself to the art of dance as a therapeutic

21

tool in every aspect, and yet she must
continue to revere her art and to cherish it
as her mainspring of inspiration" (1980).
Evan believed that the therapist's own life
experience, attitude, beliefs, and body state
were crucial to the therapy. "We don't move
with the client: we empathize with internal
muscularity; clients feel inferior, (they)
will copy you, do what you do. We want the
therapy relationship to not be the therapist
giving, doing, telling, but giving the client
responsibility and space to be what they are
in that moment" (1975). The therapist's body
(can still provide, however,) a moving
model...of possibility; expressive,
active..." (1979). When asked what was unique
in what she did with a client, Miss Evan
responded "My directness to the client. My
not accepting resistances, evasions and
certain kinds of defenses which are outworn
to the client; ways of living, thinking,
feeling. (I see) who is ready for the
additional 'sting' or 'adrenalin injection'
and who proves most often capable of making a
leap into more honesty and purpose in
handling his/her neurotic problems" (1982).

"The therapist must believe in the
client's ability to change, (but) the client
doesn't grow until the therapist grows"
(1981). She believed, and taught, that it was
essential "to leave the client alone, yet be
constructive, non-imposing, non-threatening
and non-judgmental, not (interested in)
'changing' the client; to reflect rather than
fix; to open, to find what is deeply buried"
(1978).

"One of the most important elements of
therapy is the atmosphere of sincere
acceptance, without censorship and judgement.
The therapist has to risk, as the client
does. She can't assume that a client is not

ready for a perception; she can bring the client closer to it through the tools of dance therapy and ask questions to facilitate the progress of history towards insight. The basic thread goes back to the origin, to when it began--what did the (client as a) child do to protect herself? We must retrace history to find a connection to the present. The client loses the thread. You must never lose the thread. One of the main tasks of the therapist is to untangle the tangle, and the client needs the therapist's help to do this. The purpose is not for you to change the client, but for the client to have guidelines for change, to know how to change. (It is not a question of) forcing insight onto a client, but of not accepting what is keeping a person from more fulfillment. (This requires) more risk and more honesty on the part of the client as well as the therapist" (1980).

Evan believed that her "natural, intuitive powers", as well as her life associations, self-experience and...seeing the client, (in the context of) the world around" her were forces contributing to the kind of dance therapist she was (1982). She put "stress on the import of 'dried up imagination' in the client with her cut off senses" (1982). Evan's imagination, a force (in her) as a dancer, allowed a wide field of insights in working with a client. She would ask trainees "What is your business (as a dance therapist) and what isn't?" She differentiated between therapy and counselling. "Dance therapy is not advice." A frequent statement to the client is 'that is your choice'. The therapist is there "to assist the client." She asked her trainees "What are you like? What kind of therapy do you do?" (1981). She passed on the power in her own beliefs but did not attempt to transfer them to the client.

23

Case Study

Introduction

  "Pamela's Dream"* has been slightly
modified by the editor and authors for
inclusion in this chapter. Additions for
clarity are bracketed [ ] and some sections
have been omitted purely for the sake of
brevity.

  The case of Pamela provides examples of
Evan's work on body identification, her
approaches in relating movement to content
and verbalization within the session, the
extremely selective use of recorded music,
and her emphasis on attitudes and behaviors
as well as on body movement and personal
history. The case includes an integrative
approach to the use of dream material in
dance therapy and a view of an effectve joint
effort between depth dance therapist and
verbal psychotherapist.

  Evan's relationship to the individual
client was always governed by that person's
unique condition. She would have referred to
Pamela as "more than normally neurotic"
(1982). Her decision to offer sessions of
unlimited length and to occasionally
participate in movement during the sessions
were based on her assessment of Pamela's
developmental and therapeutic needs.

---

*"Pamela's Dream, a Case History", Fall,
1962, can be read, unedited, in its entirety
in Packet of Pieces. Sedona: Blanche Evan,
1945-1978.

Other aspects of the case are well stated in Evan's own words and are included throughout the body of the case itself.

Pamela's Dream

This is a verbatum transcript of a tape presented to my inner circle of trainees in dance therapy. The long _____ means the tape could not be heard clearly.

Pamela we shall call her was a referral from a psychotherapist (whom we shall refer to as Dr. X) in the begining of her therapy. The client was twenty. She had acted, danced and modelled since the age of four.

The cast of characters:

Pamela, between twenty and twenty-five years old; a mother who drinks heavily though always holds down a job; grandmother: dead eight years; family women: aunts, cousins, half-sisters; father, in absentia for the major part of Pamela's life. She had seen him once when she was three and once when she was seven. He is now dead. Mac Crist an acrobatic teacher; Olcott, short term lover; Dr. X and three other MD's for check ups; and myself, the dance therapist.

In the interview I learned that Pamela had been a child model from the age of four years until 12. She was coerced into acrobatic dance and the ballet and theater. She was really a child bread-winner. Always subjected to criticism of her body; always disapproved of her own body. "Prayed to be thin." Much self observation in mirror, both dressed and in the nude. "Looking and wishing for a change in body contour." Grandma had acted and had been thoroughly accomplished in the theater arts. Mother had been an exhibition dancer with one of our famous ballroom studios. In a typical day, when it was time to seek a job, she said, "Well, the usual preliminaries: primed and primped for try-out."

In answer to a request to shut her eyes and give me a body image, she included every part of the body, even to the shape of the head, the length of folds, proportions, etc. But made absolutely no mention of arms and hands. When questioned, however, when she was finished describing her body image, she had a great deal to say about them, including: "Upper arm too plump, hands can be graceful but they can also be ugly during housework and drudgery, gray, old, wrinkles like alligator hide."

She described some eczema on her hands during childhood. Mother's physical actions were described with excitement. She said she had, "A perfect Yul Brynner stride" with big-boned, strong, capable hands. Pamela still thought of the theater as an exciting place. Her conception of dance therapy was muscular blocks to response. There was no thought, no feeling of movement as expression. She also indicated that she hated lying on the floor when dancing.

I believe that in this particular case, dance therapy can play a most instructive role for the patient, to replace the social criticisms, the family rejections and self-disapproval of the body, with a body image closer to her own nature and then to help rebuild it accordingly. Pamela approves of her body proportions on the whole. We set to work on what she disapproved of. She disapproved of the proportions of the

shoulder span to the rest of the body, and
when we worked, she said, "It hurts, but it's
a nice pain."

She said that she had no breath
endurance except <u>when</u> <u>she</u> <u>was</u> <u>angry</u> and in a
mad scene in the theater she could run or
perform for minutes and minutes and minutes
and never get out of breath. Hands are very
symbolic to her. Leaving hands and arms out
of the body image I think, of course, is
significant. The therapist, when I said this
to her on the phone, interpreted this in this
way: She said she cannot grasp the realities
of her life. But I say, in addition, she is
also ashamed of her hands.

I think she's ashamed, perhaps
representative of the burden of taking care
of all the house work since the age of
twelve: because when her grandmother died all
the breadwinning stopped and she became the
maid in the house; the mother went to work
and Pamela stayed home and took care of the
house at the age of twelve until the time
that she went into therapy and after. Even
when we were working on the shoulder, she
said, "It feels like I'm walking somewhere,
with my hands, that is." They're also my
mother's, who as the bread-winner and strong,
seems to be a man. "She has big bones," she
said, "whereas mine are little." Pamela's
stance is that of an over grown baby doll,
wide and inert, and her walk is weightless.

She loved the physical appearance of the
studio in this first session. She thought it
was very beautiful, and she was fascinated by
the drums: she was looking at them. I think
that when we get to playing them, this will
help in developing a positive hand and arm
strength and channel for expression of

27

aggressiveness as well as an outlet for
hostility.

My personal response to this client was
one of an all out desire to help, along the
lines described to her by me, that dance
therapy was finding the relation between the
problem and the body. From this point, I will
not say what is second, third, fourth, fifth
session, but I will give you the reports in
sequence. "How did you get along this week?"
I asked Pamela the next time I saw her. She
said, "Very well." She felt much better; she
accepted some invitations to go out and the
strain in the neck and the head seemed much
relieved, and we worked on shoulders. I asked
her about the coment she had made the last
week when she had mentioned body tension, and
I asked her now where this was. She said, a
numbness in the legs and the lower arm and a
sensation of muscles in the lower back as if
pulling apart horizontally. I said, "When?"
She said, especially after reading a long
time. I asked her to show me the position in
which she reads, and it was obvious that
circulation would be stopped in this position
because both legs were together and swung
under the hips, and the arms pressed on the
chair, and yet she had no idea that this, in
itself, would cause a blocking off of
circulation.

I suggested a different kind of position
for the following week: untwist it and I
suggested that at times she stretch out. I
asked her if there were any other times, she
said, yes: premenstrual pain. And then she
said she felt this tension in repeated
nightmares when she awakened in a cold sweat
and in the nightmare someone, and always the
same person, was in uncontrollable violence
to Pamela.

I asked the patient to walk around and if she had any image of herself walking. "None," she said. She said she had never watched herself walk. This was interesting in contrast to the detailed image of her body in static stance which she had given to me. Then she said she knew a few things about it though. For instance, she said she could not stroll and she could not stand slowness in anyone walking in front of her, and as she said this, she imitated a very sick looking creature. So I got up and walked in front of her very straight, but she said, no, the reaction was the same. She had to get in front and move faster. And she refers frequently, both last week and this, to her ability to wind in and out of crowds and to get ahead fast. She said she couldn't stand the slow walk of the choir, for instance. I asked her to run. She said it was hard to run without imagining a situation, like running after somebody.... She said that she could run for an hour after somebody in a scene. (I must say at this point that I've worked with a number of people in the theater and this should be a chapter in itself: actresses and actors in therapy.) She said again she had indefinite endurance when mad, and this I think is very very important to remember. While she was running in her typical weightless way, on two or three steps, I heard her feet on the ground, and this led to a very important revelation, because when I brought this to her attention, she said, "Oh, I never put my feet on the floor. I always walk on the toes because it's easier to move." She said, "And I have flat feet, both of them, and they are a hindrance and they are ugly."

I explained what a terrific strain she had been putting on the legs and spine and asked her to stand with her heels on the

29

ground, and she immediately showed me how the whole foot touched the ground, how ugly it was. It took no more than two minutes before I had her foot muscles working so the lifted arch was there and high enough for a pen easily to be slipped under the arch. It was agreed that she would practice this daily even when in her street shoes, and as she was doing the exercise, she pulled her hand into a very predatory position, of tremendous intensity as she was doing the arching_____. (Very young children simultaneously muscularize hand & foot, arms & legs).

Then she became self-conscious and said that this really should be a foot exercise, she thought, and I said, no. I told her again what dance therapy was, and I think this is very interesting in relation to what creative dance is in relation to what dance therapy is. I told her that she was certainly free to involve her hands emotionally when practicing her footwork at home. Then I explained how she had been carrying all her weight on the little bones of her feet for some years-- adversely working them if there were any arch problem at all.

I asked her to carry some drums. She found this very easy and I asked her to lie down and put one of our big drums on her diaphragm to see about her breathing capacity, and she had absolutely no trouble. She seemed to have tremendous breath capacity even with this big weight on her. Then she demonstrated how flexible her fingers were.

We worked on different kinds of walk the next time, basic kinds, to activate the feet. The explanation of them required a slow tempo for their doing; in order to explain to her how these walks were done, I had to do it slowly and she did it slowly. And when we sat

down, she remarked how that was the first
time she had ever enjoyed slow walking. In
each session she had mentioned her irritation
at walking behind a slow person in the
street, and her need and her ability to get
out of the situation.

I had wanted to pursue this, since tempo
is a basic element of movement, dance, and
therapy. I asked her if slow movements of any
person in any other situation bothered her
and this led at once to a description of the
movements of her mother, from which one could
conclude that Pamela's mother consumed, not
only all the space in the house, in a small
apartment where the mother throws the clothes
all over and absolutely absorbs it all, but
she also consumes all the time in the house.
And Pamela went into that further, that when
they were going to the theater, at the last
moment the cosmetic business would go on and
Pamela would watch the clock and know that
they were going to be late and there was
nothing that could hasten this woman to move.

Or when the mother took a bath, she
would stay in the tub for ages, and Pamela
would say, what can she be washing so long.
And this had been going on all of Pamela's
life. Now, I think that these points are
important because sometimes when we dance a
great deal, we are apt to think of tempo
always as beat and rhythm and so forth. But
tempo is here being used really as part of
the whole life picture, not in the sense that
we work the tempo in dance particularly, and
yet it is a very important part of dance
therapy. And I recalled an old definition of
mine about dance in which I said: "space,
time, body movement dynamics and content
welded in unity." And this is the

approach that I use always in my work in
therapy, too.

Now further discussion led to Pamela's
own expression of slowness. I asked her
certain questions and so forth. And she said
that when she was thirteen, Pamela had worked
out an effective way of losing weight because
she was so unhappy with her weight, though I
had seen pictures of her and she wasn't
really very fat. It's just that she's been
told always, that with all this weight she
wouldn't get jobs. She'd be rejected for this
play; she wouldn't get this modelling job--
and this is what had been thrown up to her
and this is what made her be so unhappy about
her weight.

So she had worked out this thing all by
herself of not eating and being inactive at
the same time, and she did lose a lot of
weight. And the mother was very angry at all
that at the time. And then in recent years,
she said that in the morning...after doing
all the chores and getting her mother out to
work, she would think of all the many things
she would do in the house the moment her
mother left, and yet the moment she did
leave, she would lie down and do nothing. She
wouldn't read. She would do nothing. And I
pointed out that this part of the slow tempo
perhaps was a protest and really a very
destructive one to herself. And perhaps her
annoyance with the slow tempo of the people
in the street might also be a protest,
destructive to her feelings about people.

We picked up the matter of the hands in
different ways, and one of the ways was this:
I suggested that she look at pictures of
hands in the arts, and this threat of her
feelings about her ugly hands of which I was
so aware in the first session...when she

32

excluded them from the body image. And so I suggested this matter to her. And she in turn mentioned the strength of her hands. She said that she could throw a telephone book, and the sound/the noise of the telephone book, "makes me want to cry."

This is important as you will see when we go on into the next session: I posed two problems for Pamela for this session: one, to assume the physical characteristics in movement of anyone who at anytime had rejected her on the basis of her bodily characteristics, as she had mentioned so often. Or, she would assume the physical characteristics in movement of her mother, as Pamela had described them so often. She had referred to her walk, for instance, and so forth. There was great resistance, but she chose the second one. She chose the mother. She said it was terribly difficult to do this because she didn't want even for a minute to be like her mother. And she had referred to her mother as the huge bulk of her, and so forth. Now, of course, when a patient says things, you don't take them at face value, but you write them down as much as you can.

She began trying by verbalizing things that she had not ever spoken of before, even to have her mother sick on the john--the intimacy in this household was complete. There was absolutely nothing of privacy. And describing other things, but only once in a while as she talked, she assumed the physical posture. And then more happened, and more enactment, and I say what a difference between words and action. For instance, when Pamela in her first session had described her mother's Yul Brynner's stride, and I asked her about that and doing that now, she got up to move but it wasn't a stride at all; it was a very funny looking trot, with her left arm

33

swinging and an accompanying verbalization of, "Oh, I must get there, oh dear, oh dear." It was really a very ridiculous picture of a big woman walking in the street.

Pamela suddenly beame aware of this and I reassured her that whatever she revealed in movement in the studio was as confidential as whatever she revealed in words to her psychotherapist. And this helped. And from that moment on, she became more and more free in enacting physical postures of her mother and then unnoticeably switched from the present to the past. I have explained that we were trying to take things out of her mind where they had been brewing and to begin to let them out through the channel of the body. She was talking and crying and enacting in full intensity, and the re-experienced three episodes one after the other in which her mother had exerted actual violence.

Her mother's words, her actions and Pamela's own physical and emotional reactions (came) all at once. She pressed her hands against her ears to shut out the harsh words--she said to protect them, "My ears always hurt," and then she enacted the action of her mother, slapping her full across the face and so strong that it spun her around as she was enacting it, remembering, "Why does she hate me so, and why am I here at all." This is what she remembered from her childhood when this incident had happened.

And then the enactment of her mother throttling her by clutching her coat collar. Now, there are more descriptions of all these incidents, more details, and I just couldn't get them down fast enough because this patient screamed out words, tears and actions. I can tell you--I was riveted against that wall. I had never seen such a

complete enactment with such intensity, with
such vividness, and such abandon as this
person exhibited. I said not a word. When it
was all over, I asked how old she had been
the last time her mother had hit her, and she
said, "When I was in junior high school I was
fifteen."

The next time she came,...she said that
after her last session with her therapist,
she felt straighter--she had no
breathlessness and she was enjoying the air
and the day, and she felt that she wanted to
get up in the morning, and she was better in
trying on dresses, and she was going about
more slowly, but in a different way. She
said, "I feel more a whole being." I told her
that we were going to concentrate on her
evaluation of her own body, who had rejected
it and why, her responses, her present ideal
and ways of accomplishing it; and that from
now on, we must work for a daily changing of
body in relation to the realistic ideal we
attained.

We reviewed the exercises and I added
some. She said she had been rejected "because
I was fat." I asked if she'd ever been called
names. "Yes," she said, "butterball face" and
"Parrel the Barrel" was a nickname.

She dieted at six years for modelling,
which started at four and until the age of
thirteen. And I gave her more exercises to
do. She said the family was very athletic,
"swinging and batting each other to hell."
Their standard, "meant more to me than
myself." And then she became very conscious
of the fact that she might go back to the
family some day and compete with them, with
her athletic cousins. She said, "Now that I
feel better, I think I could do that." Well,
I stopped her right there and pointed out

that again she was using "feeling better" to meet their standards instead of creating her own. And she caught on and she said, yes. Her body was always judged by her and others for its "commercial use." And then she said, "Beauty is to me saleable."

I questioned her and she believed this up until six months ago and I said, "Well, why did you stop?" She said because depression took over and nothing was beautiful nor saleable not anything. I discussed the disparity between her verbal description of her mother's walk i.e. the Yul Brynner stride in her first session with me and that silly little trot she had enacted in the last one. She said, "Mother's walk is divided: the Yul Brynner stride is for show, but the trot is used by her in her personal life."

Pamela feels now that she is too plump in the upper arms and she knows that some of this she says is hereditary--again, a tie up with the family. I mentioned the coming week again, her daily doing of things to change her body.

The next time when she was supposed to be here, she called instead, and said she'd gone downstairs to make the call and that she was "developing a block to these lessons." And for the last twenty-four hours she had wanted to call me to cancel but hadn't, and she had a hoarse voice because she got angry at herself, and "Mother's been sick for two days and in bed twenty-four hours a day, and the house is going to be painted in February," and she went on and on and on. I didn't say very much. I simply said, "Are you well?" She said, yes. I said, "then you could be here in half an hour." And she was here in half an hour.

Now, she had not seen her psychotherapist for about ten days, so that when
she got here, she began to talk and she
talked and talked. And she talked about
material which really did not relate to the
dance therapy work, except for about fifteen
minutes of it. However, I let it go on. She
seemed desperate in her need to talk. On the
other hand, I felt it was wrong and it didn't
belong and I knew that I would have to do
something to stop it for the future.

I explained this to Pamela. And I
explained again what dance therapy was. So,
then we spent another hour in dance therapy
material, after spending two in just her
talking this way. I tried to face her
resistance to coming and I thought, at the
time, we did accomplish a lot. Part of this
related to a new exercise I'd given her in
which I had had her lying on the floor which
had triggered her memories of Mac Crist, the
acrobatic teacher. She began to reveal a
possible sense of guilt in having enacted her
mother's violence to her and in enacting the
mother's physical characteristics which had
shown her up so poorly and I reassured her as
to the confidential relationship between the
dance therapist and the patient, and asked
her anything that bothered her in working on
the hands and she said, yes, because it
recalled her mother's hands.

I asked her if she resented my bringing
to her attention that it was time to build
her own body image and to stop competing with
images created for her by her family. She
said she had not resented it, but she really
couldn't accept it yet. She really wants no
goal at this time at all. I told her that
eventually she would have to make her choice,
her own choice, about whether she wanted to

continue to be so affected by the family in regard to her body.

Since her first life span that had been lived with other people's standards had finally led her to depressions and immobility, I could not let her blindly start another cycle of being regected for a body standard which she couldn't attain. I pointed out to her that regardless of any feeling or neurotic reasons for breaking appointments, she had social responsibilities to appointments, to me, and that if they were to be cancelled, they were to be done so in time. I think that you all know enough about therapy to understand the importance of these attitudes of mine to the patient's behavior... Instead of accepting the fact on the phone, that she wouldn't come, quite simply, I got her to come, and how important it was for what transpired. And that I saw no reason why she should not be made aware of the fact that she has responsibility, in time, to the therapist. I know all the other answers and the reasons, too, and the whys, but I feel very strongly about patients developing a sense of social responsibility and they can still fit in the transference or reasons that come up.

I then sent a note to the therapist: "Pamela's case seems to me one of antipathetic symbiosis (antipathetic being destructive and symbiosis being great dependency), her very body bound up with that of her mother's, and this is true twenty-four hours a day in the apartment in which they live. This goes into the daily routine as well into the management of the house and the cooking. (She is conflicted as) she doesn't really want to give up these chores because she takes pride in them and they make her feel superior to her mother, I think, and so forth. Now, although she knows that her mother consumes both the time and the space that at some point she will also consume Pamela if given a free rein, she is not ready to leave her mother even theoretically, and I certainly never proposed it. But I feel that the more she pulls out the injury from memory, the greater the pull to her mother will be at this time, for many reasons. And I feel that the next period of therapy in my work will be much more difficult than it has been up to now.

Pamela loved the work on the hands until her hands and actions reminded herself of her mother's hands. In other words, when she looked at her own hands, she sees her mother's. She would be perfectly willing to drop the studies in hands and art, as I have suggested; on the other hand, Pamela's hands are a symbol also to herself of inferiority-- of her mother's domination--of her house drudgery. She wants to work on beautifying her hands and she can do so only until the moment when they appear to her to be those of her mother's, and then all work is blocked.

Anything which is given to Pamela as an exercise is traumatic to her, either instantaneously or within a few hours or days and this is a girl who danced for years and years and years. This is why exposing her to...the group would be destructive to her and I would not permit her to enter a group, and I never did. Nor would she herself consent, though I have never even discussed it with her. To help Pamela best, I think it

wise to give her more opportunity at enacting
through improvisation and just forget about
the exercise at this time, not, however, to
rule out exercise, but to try to help her
disassociate from a previous experience. For
instance, to use the hand studies, to remake
Pamela's image of her hands to herself, so
that she can see them as hers and not as
those of her mother is the whole purpose of
mine in studying hands...to bring them out
into the light, because she had hidden them
in that first session.

Pamela, even when she was little, did
stand back and contemplate the reasons for
her mother's and grandmother's behavior. I
think it was this ability at objectivity
which saved her; and, therefore, I felt from
the beginning, that this had a very hopeful
prognosis. I felt the girl herself had, all
the way up, through all the torture,
exhibited a way of asking to herself, why is
this happening, why am I treated this way.
When she said, "beauty is saleable," she said
she believed this for fifteen and a half
years. I feel that her mother and grandmother
prostituted her body from the age of four to
twelve. They were well in her body. How to
help her recreate the basic evaluation of her
body, to build her own acceptable body image
for the sake of self and dignity, how to
increase her feeling of safety which was the
feeling that the psychotherapist had
suggested to me to try to instill in the
girl, in her body--how to build her self-
confidence--I think is tantamount to breaking
the symbiosis on a psycho-physical level.

Again, at the time that Pamela was due
for the next session, her mother called--this
is the first time the mother spoke to me and
she went on and on and on and on and couldn't
get a word out of me--found me very non-

40

conversant. And then Pamela got on the phone
and then finally she arrived a half hour
later, and her mother called again to see if
Pamela had arrived. It was all explained and
in fact, the mother had given her fifteen
cents for the bus so she wouldn't take a
taxi, and very interesting, the girl asked
the doorman for money and came in a cab
anyway.

I explained to Pamela that I thought she
was permitting her mother to make Pamela into
her own image, to make her slow up, to make
her late, for the theater, and for this and
for that and for getting out of the house,
and so forth. This is just what Pamela had so
often resented and yet she was letting her
mother make her into the same kind of slow
getting out from the purpose. We enacted
it together--I think I got in front of her
and it kind of hypnotized her, although I
know nothing about hypnosis. But I just
walked in front of her, like this, and she
just walked backwards and we walked like that
and she knew, much better than I could say in
words, what I meant by this insidious kind of
influence that the mother was wielding over
her.

Pamela spoke of the horrible three
nights in a real nightmare she had had, which
was a little bit of what you saw. She had
awakened this morning with a terrible pain in
the back of her neck, her arms out and her
hands clamped in a kind of rigor mortis, with
her left hand lifeless and paralyzed. From
this point on, just as in the enactment of
her mother's violence, she talked so fast and
so much, that it was impossible to take it
down, but this was the best I could do, and
everything I write now is a quote:

"A group of women, a whole family of women want something out of me; they are after me. Somebody is doing something with their arms. Heavy legs all of them, coming toward me, going to do something to me, who is where, who is where, brunettes and gray hair and woke up with the name of my cousin on my lips and my mother's first cousin and there was a white house with a black and a family gathering and everybody's going to get into one big fight in a room and I'm very small.

"There are two couches and a big lamp and a chair and I's trying to hide out mother or grandmother says, 'do come here and talk to so and so--do, dear, come here and do this and this and the other--and do come and do this and that'--(in deep commanding voices which I cannot imitate)--and then an uncle and aunt and the house disappears--and people are standing--and it's cold, terribly cold-- and I have to go to the toilet. And their mouths are moving and their voices are not individual--all from the person but more as if the sky were talking--and then enough, and as small as I could get and I want to be underneath the ground." (And, of course, she was talking and crying at the same time, but she hadn't done anything with her body.)

I had tried to get Pamela to enact her nightmare but she was in a terribly agitated state and I felt that I must pull her back to the physical reliving in her body--of the nightmare. So I became very firm and said, "Stop talking and move," which she did, and very soon after, while she was dancing out the nightmare, she broke into free tears which didn't happen when she was talking, and she went on moving and talking and crying.

42

At this point, when she was wanting to be under the ground, tied in a knot, I pulled that blanket out, which is magic in the studio--it's worked in a thousand different ways--and I threw it to her and she buried the upper part of her body under it and around it, lying on the floor that way. Then she went on talking: "For oblivion, nothingness, gray, no feeling, lightness, touching yourself and you are yourself or have other people bother me--I don't want to touch myself with my hands and have the entire--hands must feel my body like a corpse--I'd be plaster--smoke--heavy as in the texture of smoke."

When she was finished I asked her to look at her hands. She said, "Reddish-white knuckles--they're dry and red--and I see two spots on them and there are five fingers and a palm." And I asked her about the color of her nail polish. Don't ask me why. I don't know why I asked her that. She said, "Frosty pink." And I said, "Your mother's?" "Dried blood red," she said. And then with a horrible cynical gesture she added, "Victory red." I asked her to press her hands on her face and touch it. She said, "face is cold, mealy-like, like cold oatmeal. It's really hot now and flushed but my hands are an entity--my skin is grainy--textured wall paper--in the dream I still want to touch my body--I haven't liked it for so long."

I asked her when she could remember the first time she didn't like her body and she said, "When I had my first cold and I was all stuffed up and I couldn't cry or talk or drink water or breathe, and there were bars on the crib." I said, "How old?" "Two years old," she thought. I said, "were there clamps on the crib blanket--the words that you used to describe your arms when you woke up out of

43

your nightmare." She said, "yes, yes, yes--that seems right." And she went on about a tall doctor being there and so forth. "Yes," she said, "the clamps--it doesn't seem right--and I was always tucked in with the clamps. I was always tucked in and until seven and a half I sucked the second and third fingers of my right hand, sucking and hiding under the blanket, while the other hand pulled little bits from the blanket."

I asked Pamela again to look at her hands and to try to see hers instead of her mothers. And she said, "when I was about six and a half or so, I was more feminine then--like my last year in high school. I don't know where that went, I don't understand what masculine is--not feminine, nor masculine--I feel like an oddity."

Then Pamela said to me, "You asked me to see myself through my mother's eyes and I tried it, and I came to the bosom sticking out like a shelf, her bosom is so big she can't see anything beyond it, and all the women in the family are that way." She said, "Mine are so small." She said, "They're all masculine women--like the prow heads the ships, sort of sailing. Grandmother's walk," and she began to move again,--stomp--stomp--stomp very strong steps with a side to side movement of her shoulders--up and down, too, as a man might have. She said, "Grandma could look like a man walking beside me or with me--her face is that of a man." And she spoke about picking at her body after grandma died. And I said, "Did it hurt?" And she said, "Yes, at times." She said, "It was like trying to get something out of my body." She said before ten she had had a mole. She said that grandma had lots of them thousands of them--"I had only some." So I said, "Were you

pleased that you had only some or would you
have rather had lots like grandma?" She said,
"That's fantastic your saying that. Because
just yesterday I was looking at this big spot
(which is part of a skin illness that she
had) and I thought how that was the exact
place on the inside of my right ankle where
grandmother had had it also, just as
grandma," she said.

"My voice and quality are sometimes the
same as in mother's words. Then I want to
kick her" ... and Pamela gave her leg a free
swinging, hard kick, she said, "So she'd land
on her face. I want to kick her right between
where it hurts" (which, of course, is a very
masculine image, because it's like hitting
the scrotum, and she too, then, was really
thinking of her mother as a man.) She said,
"A year and a half ago I slapped her ..." And
I said, "Had you slapped her at any other
time?" And she said, "yes, when she was lying
there in her lover's apartment, drunk like a
big bloated baby." I said, "A girl or a boy
baby?" She said, "A girl. Mother could be
very feminine when she dressed to go out and
with beautiful clothes and then I wanted to
possess her, to be with me, and not for her
to go out and look that way for somebody
else."

When I had gone into the dressing room
to call Pamela for the beginning of her
session, I found her doing an exercise on the
floor, and I explained to her that today her
free time had been spent really in dance
therapy to her advantage. She said, "Yes,"
(that) last week...she had been very
disappointed after the session because there
had been no physical action. I'm so glad that
I pulled her verbalizing today into action--
really making her move when she would have

45

not moved without really being pushed into
it.

I explained to Pamela what all the
material seemed to confirm, that her body was
so much part of her mother and grandmothers,
that our task was to find her own. "Well, that
might be so," but it was no use just using
that as a delay mechanism, for the problem
that faced us was in finding the self
identity. She then recalled how, when she
practiced the piano when she was a little
girl, her left hand--you remember the left
hand?--couldn't manage the bass and
grandmother had sat there always with a stick
and rapped her knuckles with it, I said, "The
same hand that was paralyzed this morning
when you woke up after the nightmare?" She
said, yes, the same. I asked Pamela to try
very hard if the nightmare happened
again,...to use her arms and hit out with
them. She has said that in her dreams she can
never move to defend herself.

I asked her to try to dream moving in
the dream and when I discussed my suggestions
with the psychotherapist, she approved of the
suggestions (I suggested them first and
discussed them later) but I did really always
want to check with her.

Pamela, the next time, said that
yesterday, for the first time, she had looked
out of the window, participating with the
scene, and she felt she was beginning to deal
with things; these are her words: "deal
with--contend with--and adjust." She was
closer to stopping rationalizing and
replacing this (defense) by feeling. I did
not question her about this. She mentioned
how many devices she had resorted to in her
life, "How not to cry." And she spoke of not
being away from home, but "out of it," and

that she had belonged to "two women and was manipulatd by them, like on a string." I brought up the use of the words duality and plurality in the previous session. Pamela said she was referring to the action of our session because she felt so tense (she was building a block to coming here) and yet she wanted to, and that's the sense of duality with her, and she doesn't know why. When I said "and plurality", she said, "Oh, that's an embellishment,..." That's what I mean about people attached to the theater--the watching out for the thing that creeps in-- that is realy theatrical. This is perfectly valid because that's been a major part of their life; and, I'm sure, if a dancer were in movement therapy, there would be a great deal there that one would have to realize came out of dance and perhaps was a layer above the therapeutic situation.

Most of all, I wanted to explore her reference to herself as an oddity. She said, "Mother had explained when I was nine or ten, that men are the stronger sex, and that men always disappointed mother because they never lived up to their promise, not their potential, but their promise. And also, all the marriages had been unhappy ones-- grandmother's, mother's, and aunts, and so forth." She adds, "Sex--a disturbing role. Being an oddity--where do you start from-- feeling neuter is a shield that is always there." She said there was safety in it-- something to hold onto. "So when I see girls tittering," (and by that I think she meant coy or feminine) she said, "I resent it because if I tried to act feminine, I might not know how to." And this is Pamela's world who for all the world looks like a budding woman, there is nothing masculine in this girl's appearance at all.

Now we hadn't referred to Olcott before, but this was a short term love affair that she had had that meant a lot to her. I said that, "Olcott brought out your feminity." She said, yes, and she had enjoyed it. And I tried to refer to the "massive, big bosomed women" that she'd always mentioned; and she said, "I can't understand men. These masculine women, like mother and grandmother, say they are capable of doing anything a man can do; they pick out weaknesses in men and exaggerate them because they feel inadequate as women." (She had analyzed all this--this was pretty wonderful.)

"Even grandmother, who had three older brothers, and was daddy's little girl, competed, so that eventualy she could outrun her brothers and this frustrated them."

Of course, these were very castrating women, and, either she was too weak, in the sense that she felt too inadequate to cope with them, (maybe that saved her) or, she was strong, (and I really think it was the strength--from everything that I know about her.) In any case, she really didn't want to accept the standard for herself of a masculine woman. She said, "The women's masculinity--all my senses were touched by them--hearing the loud, deep voices, seeing their walk and feeling grandmother's hand on my shoulder or on my back, and my mother's hand on my face when I was slapped, and grandma pushing me. I had to be important. I wanted to be something. I had to be. But I was born second best because I was a girl."

I said to her, "Femininity to you is a big risk. Yet you enjoyed your feminine role with Olcott and your femininity in your last year at high school, as you had mentioned."

She said, yes, and she clings to this short love experience that she had had. Then I asked her a few questions and to please answer the very first thing that came into her head. I said, "What is the worst thing that ever happened to you?" And she said immediately and self-consciously, "Well, my mind is a blank. I don't know what happened. There are two or three people in a light, new dress and I am extremely small and they are very big."

And from this point on I will refer to the nightmare very often, though I didn't refer to it when I spoke with Pamela. Because in the nightmare, of course, she is extremely small, that is a thing that is so terrifying to her, that she winds herself up in a knot and gets under the ground. And I asked, "Now that you think out the question, what is the worst thing that ever happened to you, instead of an immediate response, what is your answer?" She said, (and again it was the incident of her mother) "My mother washing the clothes and she slapped me across the face when I was nine. I couldnt move. But I had to move to get out of her violence and I was terrified. I couldn't move." That, too, was in her nightmare--"I couldn't move."

I said, "What is the thing you want most in the world?" And she said, "Round. Something round and nebuluous and soft." And I said, "If you think it out?" And she said, "Well, I want a father and a country and a big house." (Now, that was in the nightmare, too). She said, "Life is hell. It's a lot of bull and a disappointment."

I said, "Can you formulate what you would like your therapy to lead to? And to work out." This is her answer: "The confusion about myself. What to do. I want to be

49

something in between--neuter, it, sexless. It's strange and peculiar--neither boy nor girl. I didn't know until the second or third grade that thereafter, grandmother dressed me in many clothes--clothes--clothes--under corduroy pants I was boxed in--what was she keeping away--other little girls were dressed in cute frills above their knees and Mary Janes--how I wanted frills and Mary Janes-- even the household was strange, living in one room." (She named the girl friends that she's had in the seventh and eighth grades, searching to find out why they were feminine.) I asked her how long she had had this break out on her skin and she told me a long time. And I said, "You'd mentioned something on your arms." It seems that at various times her skin had reacted to her emotional problems.

Then she said, in the fourth and fifth grades, for two and a half years, she had had a fungus between the thumb and the first finger on the writing hand and then she explained that her grandmother had forced her to practice the Palmer system of penmanship every day for hours.

I had determined that no patient would leave a session without working physically. I told Pamela I had pepared a few moving projects; and if the first one was not good for her to do today, I would suggest the others; but she wanted the first! It was based on part of her last week's when enacting "being little" she had, after a moment on her haunches, stood up...and I had insisted that she enact it really crouched down, making herself as little as possible.

She said it's harder to be little. So I went back to this and I drew the analogy for her...that it really was harder for her to be

her age and little, just as it was physically
with her body to really be little. She was
sitting hunched over on the floor with her
legs up to her chest--"and six inches across
the back, an inch long here, four inches
high, my head is down, I remember being that
small, I had been bathed and was standing on
the john, and both parts were down and I was
standing being dried and I slipped and I fell
down between the wall and the john--I was so
scared I couldnt cry. I tried to say
something and couldn't," and as she enacted
this, she was really trying to make the
effort to make a sound--it was all so real to
her. "And my chest was so constricted--I
couldn't breathe, and grandmother and mother
standing there, hysterically laughing."

I asked her if any comfort or any kind
of help had been forthcoming because (as a
therapist) you don't (automatically) accept
this kind of complete rejection. And she
said, yes, she had remembered a look of
concern on her mother's face and she imitated
it. Then she want on, "I spread my legs for
room, because I was only two or three or four
years old, and they picked me up, and instead
of crying, I urinated." (At the end of her
nightmares, she'd always run to the toilet.)
She said, "I don't remember if they laughed
at that or when I was on the floor, I was
small and squished, and later on in school at
a desk, I felt small and squished this way,
and I hurt the lower part of my back in the
fall." (You remember that that's where she
gets tension.) "And my feet were cold and
wet, and I had a terrible fear." And then she
said, "I must have been that small, otherwise
how could I get down there between the wall
and the john?"

Of course, the intensity was now broken, this was an extremely intense experience, on the same level of intensity as the others. So she said, "How could I get down there," unless she was small; and then she turned around to herself and she said, "Now, Pamela, don't try to get down behind the toilet." This statement is very interesting because it showed certainly a self-destructive tendency, even though she was aware of this, and (related it to) suicidal thoughts at times in her life.

And again it showed this characteristic that I found so wonderful in her, of being able to look at something and see it and here it was again. And then she went on, "It is fantastic how small I can be. I'm in a play pen in the Adirondacks, trying to stand on my head, and I saw blue spots and bitter nausea and poison coming into my mouth and through my nose, making myself sick," (Again, this self-destruction)"...looking through the bars of the play pen and my cousin laughing at me, and then in my crib making funny faces at my cousin and he laughing--already they were laughing at me.".... She really felt that the world of adults that she knew had only contempt for her. I put on some music on. She said, "It reminds me of a rocker we had, that looked like a witch; it had become alive and I'd hide--the cat(?) coming at me from each corner; (as in the nightmare again.)

She had actually had this rocker and she was so terrified of it, it had taken on the appearance of a witch at night, and things were coming at her from each corner, just as in the nightmare. Something alive in the closet and moving, closing in on all sides and other dreams of insects and so forth. She said, "I wanted to scream but I couldn't," (again that terrible frustration.) And her right hand fisted, "I wanted to scream but I couldn't." It really seemed like a real frustration at not being able to attack.

I tried to separate what was experienced, what was the night dream and what was fantasy. She said, "No, the fantasies were day dreams, and they have always been pleasant things." So we had actually not gone into them during the thin body, and so forth. And as with most children in our society, it's all television; but, of course, in her case, you see, she lived in this house with these two women and all this terror going on in the television, and then she said, "Actually, once a month I at least murdered one person." And then she would watch some more, and the whole place became filled with terror which by the way, she got over with only after the grandmother died, and she had thrown out much in the house and redecorated it (while) still a young child..... In one dream, "I was a huge human being," and, of course, this is marvelous.

I had told Pamela that if I could put into one word the crux of her dance therapy, it was "separation", the physical separation of her body from the body of her mother and grandmother. I twisted my fingers with both hands and said, "When one does this, often one cannot tell which is her own left;...you know, you get mixed up: you don't know which is your finger after awhile. I tore the hands apart and demonstrated how, of course, each hand then was smaller than the entwined hand, and that was where we had to start. She now acknowledged the entwinement and the physical breaking of the umbilical cord at the age of twenty and a starting out, not little and stifled, but little, her self growing, her own body, and stance, and so forth. I elaborated on this and she grasped the whole

53

thing. "That I can say about my body, 'it's mine!' I never before thought about it in those words. When I say it, I can hear my voice, 'it's me!' At other times my body doesn't feel, and I don't hear myself when I talk." She had described how little she had felt, she said, "My arms are not long enough to reach, and my legs can't run fast enough, and I'm very litttle around my neck."

This attitude of mind to her littleness is very important, I think, very very important in the course of her therapy, because I had no desire just to make her feel that she was a big girl. No, to herself she really was very little, but she needed to recognize that this little thing which came from the separation, has the potential of now growing up into a person of her own size. I mentioned again her identity of parts of her body with her mother's, as in the hands. "Yes, my palm looks like an infant's. And in our sessions, when I looked at some of these art hands, I was reminded of my mother's hands. Her palm is soft and fleshy and white blood-celled that can envelope and eventually asorb and whisk it away." I say she is alerted of being careful of being consumed by her mother and I reinforced this idea in some discussions.

She began to move around the room, walking. She said, "Do you notice anything different in my walk?" I said, "It seems natural." She said, "Yes--my feet." And she pointed to them and displayed a very good arch, and she remembered about her flat foot theory, which she had talked about in the first session. She said, "And my hips are moving when I walk, as a woman's does." She said, "I never walked that way before." And she went to the bar and she did a plie, and she exclaimed, "I'm alive! My hips are no longer granite, as I felt them to be in every dancing lesson I ever had." You remember in the nightmare she talked of her body being plastic. She said, "I can back bend, and the hurt in the lower back and the fear is gone. I could never do back bends. The lower back isn't destroying the connection between the hips and the upper back. I never had any feeling in the back. Who hammered it in? And I'm little and little and little and my arms don't have to be longer than they are to function."

I was reminded of my impression in the first session of her stance as that of an inanimate doll, and now, for the first time, I found a connection with the plaster and the granite that I didn't know about at that time. (This is very interesting because as a dance therapist what you see and what it means to you and how you utilize it can take a long time until it becomes explained and validated. Then you know your sight was right even though you didn't know the reasons for it.)

And this matter of her body being an inanimate or doll like was very very important. Now the change into a human being moving about was so startling, that to help believe it, I remembered cases of hysteria and recalled the disappearance of the physical defect--it was almost as much of a change as that. She spoke of the inner confidence since her last session, when she was with her mother, and that she loses this confidence when she's alone. I spoke of the necessity for changing the style of life, an Adlerian term, which is very good and useful--in small daily patterns. For instance, she had developed the habit of never being dressed in the house, but always being in a robe, and when she had spoken of not being able to stand any more of...the nagging of her mother I said, simply, "Well, why don't you go out--go for a walk?"

She said, "Well, I can't. I'm not dressed." And this change, a simple change in her style of life in the household, was very important, because what happened was that she began to be dressed all the time, which, in itself, was a very good thing. It gave her much more of a sense of dignity and she felt always ready to take herself out of this situation, and the result was a lot of the nagging stopped, because her new independence and her new appearance and attitude, of course reacted upon her mother. Before she left that session, her sinuses began to flow out free, one Kleenex after another, and I recalled her enacting her scenes in the pen when she was standing on her head...making herself sick, in her own words, and so forth, and I felt this might have been a very definite tie up to that which had occurred.

The next session, Pamela seemed a new Pamela today. She was relaxed and enthusiastic. She walked in with a big shopping bag of pictures and showed me all the pictures of her whole family, and it was very interesting because I was sure that I had met her grandmother--I knew exactly--she looked exactly the way I had imagined her. And now I will tell you something which is even more interesting than that.

Pamela had associated me with her grandmother, and I didn't know this until after the therapy had ceased, and she had lost it only a month and a half before we terminated the therapy. And we had a discussion about it and she said, "Well, it was mostly because it was my grandmother who was with the dancing all the time." And some of this was hard for her to take. And I asked her was there anything pleasant and she told me that she felt sweet things about her grandmother, too. It must have been because otherwise she could not have given so much in the therapy session.

Now her mother, too, looked as if I had seen her somewhere, but not so much as the grandmother. The father looked young--had a dreamy look. And Pamela said that he might have been a dreamer, but he...had influenced her idea of beauty being saleable because she knew that her father was always selling things.

The pictures of herself in childhood, just broke me up because she had the most beautiful eyes and the most beautiful round body--not fat and tubby at all but just beautiful...(When I saw) her being dressed in all these ghastly show costumes, her whole story really was most piteous.

She said that when she got back to the apartment that day, that she had felt little, "but," she said, "everything in the apartment looked smaller." She said before that she had felt bigger, but everything in the apartment was bigger than she. She said, too, that the space in the apartment had changed; it had more air in it now. The mother had changed certain of her habits, of possession, and, she said, "There is no mustiness in the air," (and that is purely psychological.)

I asked how long this "little" feeling had lasted and she said three or four days. "It's more natural now to be little, feeling young,--I'm not forty-five." She spoke of her dreams; the nightmares ceased.

57

She said the dreams were now, "My size with my friends--no family--Olcott was in some of them...

She said that when her mother came near to wake her, she had accidentally stepped on Pamela's glasses and Pamela had warned her that if she ever did that again, she'd get the biggest kick she'd ever had in her life." She said, "Mother went over neatly and sat down in a chair and looked frightened." I asked Pamela if she had retained the softness of body motion since the last session. She said, yes. And I suggested dancing to music for the very first time and she danced with a wonderful limberness and she did very difficult floor acrobatics without any sense of strain emotionally or physically. She did back bends and balances and she was just lovely to watch....

Pamela is no longer neuter. She is feminine. She has separated her body from her mother's and her family's. Her body is now a different shape from what it had been before. Pamela's hands now exist to herself. They are now graceful, expressive and functionally stronger. Pamela's concept of her littleness has changed to one of height.

Now, I would say that if sessions had been of a regular time, this would have taken about thirty weeks. Because the sessions were several hours long, it was condensed into about three months. There was a wonderful force in this girl, a bravery and desire for self-preservation, she could not go on living as she had.

The constant interchange of thought between me and the psycotherapist was a great factor in what we were working toward: At my end of it my interpretation of mother dependency, and interdependency was crucial as being a physical symbiosis, to the extent of body being body. She always combed her mother's hair every morning. I remember asking her what she felt when she combed her mother's hair. There was no moment in that house where those two bodies weren't one. My feeling that the physical thing needed to be broken, was, I felt, the most important contribution that I had to make to this therapy. Also my use of the basic element of stance. Characteristics of these dance therapy sessions were the use of enactment in silence rather than improvisations, no use of drums and almost none of music. I used acute sight, picking up indications of body movement or body in taking risks for the choice of the enactment, even though the material was so traumatic to the patient.

I did permit what seemed at times excessive verbalizations for a dance therapy session, but reached a point, when I made it a rule that no session be concluded without having used physical expression or physical movement even if this were outweighed in time by verbalization. No patient would leave this room without relating with the body. I used tempo and area to help me interpret the material rendered by the patient. And I used such concepts as life style changes, even though these would be changes that would seem to relate to symptomatic changes rather than to growth changes. I used dance of other cultures or arts of other cultures to aid in one important area, that of her hands....

In passing, I would say that the violence of the mother through the years, in the end helped Pamela far more than an inactive hostility on the mother's part, or an over-charged deceptive sweetness of over-protection might have done. Because at least when the time came, Pamela had something to hit out at. As with her "flat feet", I did not accept the patient's impressions of her own body image as reality. Until my objective had been achieved I set no limits on the time of the session, even when they ran to three hours and longer. No extra fee was charged for the extra time. My objectives in the case: primarily to help Pamela create self-identity in her body, secondarily, to help Pamela change her feeling from being neuter and an oddity to being a self-accepting female. Some of these changes were root changes. Some of them were symptomatic changes. Some of them were life style changes. I think that the enactment of these nightmares and the john came closer to root enactment and possibility led to very basic changes. I don't underestimate the value of those enactments. I would be very foolish to do so because when I asked Pamela, at the end of everything, what had been the most important session to her, it was that--she had no trouble in finding the answer. Nor do I wish to underestimate the value of symptomatic changes in the person's life.....

The enactment of recall, or a better way to say it, recall of an action and enactments of physical characteristics of those people who had rejected Pamela: of her mother and grandmother who had exploited her proved something that a great psychiatrist once said and it was this: "All the life experiences, the inner life history, takes part in the elaboration of the body image. Now, inner life history is also the history of our relation to our fellow human beings and the community in its broadest sense."

Bibliography

Ansbacher, H. and R. The Individual
Psychology of Alfred Adler. N.Y.: Harper
and Row, 1956.

Brody, Jane E. "Emotions Found to Influence
Nearly Every Human Ailment," New York
Times, May 24, 1983.

Evan, Blanche. Brochure of the Dance Therapy
Centre. N.Y.: Blanche Evan, 1969.

_____. The Child's World: Its Relaton to Dance
Pedagogy. N.Y.: St. Marks Editions,
1949-1951.

_____. "Introductory Remarks for the 'Flow of
Therapy'," 1967. In Packet of Pieces.
Sedona: Blanche Evan, 1945-1978.

_____. "...the Least Movement of the Body."
The Journal of Pastoral Counseling,
Spring, 1970.

_____. Packet of Pieces. Sedona: Blanche Evan,
1945-1978.

_____. Personal Communications between 1970-
1982.

Melson, Barbara. "Body Image and Its Relation
to Self Concept in Individual Dance
Therapy with a Normal Adult Male,"
unpublished Master's thesis, Hunter
College, 1980.

Rifkin-Gainer, Iris. Unpublished "Interview
    with Blanche Evan," University of
    Illinois, Urbana, 1969.
_____. "An Interview with Blanche Evan,"
    American Journal of Dance Therapy, 1982,
    Volume 5, pp. 5-17.

Object Relations and Self Psychology within Psychoanalytic and Jungian Dance-Movement Therapy

Penny Lewis Bernstein Ph.D., ADTR*
Arlene Avstreih MS, ADTR**

Genesis

To speak of the evolution of my work as a dance therapist is to speak of the evolution of myself for the two are intricately related. Simply, movement has been for me the source and expression of my most authentic self. It has been the expression of my joys, my struggles and my

---

*Penny Lewis Bernstein began a six year Jungian analyst-in-training program at the C. G. Jung Institute of New York in 1982. She is the co-editor of the Choreography of Object Relations and currently trains and supervises graduate dance therapy students in an object relational Jungian analytic approach and is in private practice in depth movement psychotherapy in the Boston area. The Psychoanalytic and Jungian Object Relations Theory sections, as well as the case study in Jungian Object Relations, were written by her.
**Arlene Avstreih is a dance therapist and psychoanalyst in New York City and Eastchester, N.Y. She is the past coordinator of the Graduate Dance Therapy Program at Pratt Institute and is the author of several articles in the field. The Genesis and Psychoanalytic Object Relations case study sections were written by her.

sorrows. Most strongly, it is my connection
with the creative energies of life.

Shortly after completing my masters
degree in dance therapy, I decided to train
as a Psychoanalyst. Even as a beginning
therapist, I had been keenly aware of what I
later learned to understand as transference.
I was always aware that a person's movement
could not be separated from the total
experience of their being. More and more, I
came to realize that each person's unique
life experience and self perceptions would be
re-enacted in the therapeutic relationship.
By working through the transference aspect of
the relationship, the movement changes could
become integrated within the tonality of the
person. In this way, psychic changes and
restructuring are achieved, not merely split-
off movement of learned behavioral
alterations.

My training as an analyst coincided with
a very exciting period of psychoanalytic
evolution: the exploration of Self
Psychology. Developmental theory was looking
further and further back into infancy,
gaining more and more clarity of how an
infant develops into the unique person he or
she becomes.

It seems when we talk about the self, we
are talking about a continuity of being, a
primary sense of existing. Just as each
embryo needs the placenta to grow in and be
nourished by, each infant needs the holding
environment of an emphatic object to continue
to grow and to develop a sense of being. Thus
the paradox of self is that it requires
another. All that the infant brings with it
into the world becomes molded in the
interaction of the early maternal
environment. Through my work with clients and

my own experience of motherhood, it became clear that the self is the choreographic product of the unique dance between each infant and mother, which, of course, becomes further elaborated by the father and significant others.

Mahler (1975) refers to the infant as the infant of a particular mother, emphasizing the mother's role in response to the infant as essential in creating the particular infant of that mother. I have come to believe through my direct clinical experience that the cueing process, the dance, is much more mutual. Each particular infant/client evokes certain aspects of a given mother/therapist. Through my training and supervision of graduate dance therapy students, this premise continued to be revalidated. Thus the more able the mother/therapist is to clearly see the unique infant/client in front of her, free from her own projections and past unmet needs, the more her image of her infant/client will coincide with his/her actual being. The accurate and reality-congruent mirroring response of the mother/therapist provides a continuity of being: that which we call self.

The empathic object is internalized as a sense of well-being and is the foundation for the sense of being able to care for oneself and later to love and nurture another. When the early mothering is either unresponsive or impinging, there is a jolt to the sense of continuity and a too early awareness of "separateness" and "other". These repeated experiences are internalized as pathological introjects. The earlier and the more disruptive the process, the less there is a continuous sense of self. Instead, there are fragments, a sense of disruption, panic and terror.

The very early sense of self is closely related to bodily sensations including both internal experiences of the infant and the ministrations of the mother. When the environment has been severely disruptive, the body itself is experienced as an enemy because it houses a predominance of negative introjects and an overabundance of unneutralized aggression. I have come to see that the greater the student/intern/ therapist's capacity to contain, reorganize, and detoxify this negativity, the greater the possibility for a more realistic sense of body self.

Thus I came to know that as a therapist, I must not only be an empatic, reliable object, but must appropriately work with the pathological introjects as they appear in the transference and resistance, for these introjects severely distort reality and prevent the internalization of more positive, nurturing self/object representations. At times, my empathic response is experienced as painful for the patient. It is almost as if love and care have become conflictual states of being; for these patients to have gained their mother's love meant they had to deny their own needs for nurturance. The caring reminds them that they were either not permitted or forced to separate at too early an age. Intense feelings of rage and vulnerability are evoked.

As therapist, I need to also be prepared for the present-day rage. As I work through the projections, I am experienced as more and more separate by the patient. This phenomena also evokes rage because it undermines the patient's desire to deny the initial loss and subsequent self-hate for causing the rejection. The relinquishing of the omnipotent fantasy for reunion with the all-

66

loving mother leads to a deep mourning
process and a resolution of loss which can
result in the completion of the separation-
individuation process--a true psychological
birth for these patients.

Conceptual Genesis and Its Relation to Dance-Movement Therapy

The growing interest in object relations
theory reflects an ever strengthening trend
in the advancement of psychoanalytic thought
and practice. As target populations for depth
therapy expanded in age range to encompass
children as well as adults, and in diagnoses
to include character disorders and psychoses
as well as neurotic dysfunctions, the role of
the therapist within the treatment process
has broadened. Summarizing the international
trend, Dewald (1976) has observed that, "the
conceptual understanding of the role of the
analyst in psychoanalytic process has
undergone a continuing expansion away from
the images of the neutral passive, non-
participant mirror who merely provides the
patient with insight through interpretations.
Increasingly, the psychoanalytic situation is
seen as an active and evolving process
between two participants" (pp. 215-216).

This orientation in therapy with
children was spearheaded through the
pioneering work of Margaret Mahler and D. W.
Winnicott. Its application to adults has been
largely influenced by Heinz Kohut, in the
United States, and by Ronald Fairbairn, D. W.
Winnicott and Harry Guntrip in England. It is
the work of these object relations theorists
together with Jungian object relations
analysts, Michael Fordham in England and
Nathan Schwartz-Salant in the U.S. that is
being applied to and integrated with the

practice of dance-movement therapy in this chapter.

The Freudian analysts can be viewed as expanding upon ego psychology and Sullivan's (1953) interpersonal theory. Ego psychologists such as Anna Freud (1966), Heinz Hartmann (1958), and Erik Erikson (1963) have demonstrated the importance of each phase of sequential development in the organization and well being of an individual. Each previous phase is seen as providing a foundation or building block for subsequent stages in life. Instead of grouping all early conflicts into a "preoedipal" category, Anna Freud (1966) brought out oral and anal issues from their "secondary" relegation and conceptualized several other crucial lines of development. Building on her work, Erikson (1963) emphasized psychosocial development in his "Eight Stages of Man" giving these all equal value. Sullivan (1953) highlighted the importance of the self, its origins in interpersonal life, and the need to maintain stability of the self-system in interpersonal relations throughout life.

Although Jungian analysts acknowledge the importance of interpersonal relations and ontogeny, the view of the Self as a priori and not confined to cause and effect phenomena is categorically different than the psychoanalytic view. The concept of identity as emerging from merger, projection, and introjection is seen as limiting in its perspective.

Natural introversion plays at least as strong a role as the extrovertedly based interpersonal focus with the organizing function of the Self outweighing the view of the therapist as a prime director of the process.

Due to a need for increasing sophistication in the understanding of how the primary etiology of pathological structures develops, object relations theorists of both Freudian and Jungian orientations began to focus with great detail upon the first three years of life. These beginning years have been held under a magnifying glass, as it were, to better understand the specific needs and therapeutic requirements of individuals with early wounds. A growing clinical literature suggests that autistic and psychotic children, psychotic adolescents and adults, those with borderline conditions and pathological narcissism, as well as the retarded and developmentally disabled, have all benefited from this frame of reference, while other theoretical approaches have met with relative failure.

The field of dance-movement therapy has paralleled much of the development of object relations theory and self psychology. The needs that have drawn these theoretical perspectives into the foreground of depth psychology have also drawn dance-movement therapy from a fledgling profession in the early sixties to a viable field of psychotherapy. Many of the same concerns regarding the treatment of the populations mentioned earlier brought dance therapists into clinical institutions (Bernstein, 1979) and onto the referral list of more traditional depth therapists who could not effectively treat individuals with severe characterological difficulties (Siegel, 1979).

Movement therapists have long understood and utilized the premise that body movement is the most primary means of communication. From a cognitive point of view, the most fundamental level of organizing and integrating developmental phases is through enactive cognition where body felt experience and movement interaction are the prime sources of learning. Long before an infant understands what is being said verbally or even on an iconic level, responds to visual cues, s/he feels the nuances of the mothering person's physical ministrations. Memories of these early experiences are on a pre-verbal level since the central nervous system has not sufficiently developed for more sophisticated verbal memories during the early months of life. Winnicott writes of this early symbiotic phase that it is "pre-verbal, unverbalized, and unverbalizable" (1971, p. 130). Thus, unconsciously derived movement rather than more traditional verbal responses have been found to elicit the associational remembering and re-experiencing of the object relations phenomena that often needs to take place (Greenson, 1967).

The dance-movement therapist has been trained to relate to and respond to the client at this most basic body-movement level. The therapist's ability to translate the body posturing, breathing, and movement in terms of developmentally based object relations facilitates the development of transference and the subsequent working through of early wounds. It was, and is, the dance-movement therapist that is often referred individuals who, either due to organic dysfunction or functional regression, are on a non-verbal level of interaction. Experience has shown that autistic, psychotic and/or organically disabled persons have, indeed, been able to deeply engage in the therapeutic process with the movement therapist. Although many movement therapists are initially hired as adjunctive therapists, the potential of these techniques often brings them and their work to primary therapeutic focus.

The following discussion attempts to integrate the major Freudian and Jungian object relations theorists with movement therapy theory and techniques and to elucidate the direct relationship between the fundamental premises and work within the field of dance-movement therapy and object relations theory. Two case studies will exemplify the Jungian and Freudian object relational perspectives in movement therapy.

Theoretical Model: Objective Relations Theory within a Psychoanalytic and Ego Psychological Perspective

Concepts

View of the Individual

In 1971, Harry Guntrip wrote, "It is naive to think of a primitive id dictating to a socialized ego or vice versa. We must think of a psychosomatic whole person in whom the fate of the organism is far more completely determined by psychic self. The psychic self uses the body for both symbolic self expression and for direct action and for both together as a psychosomatic whole" (pp. 86-87). This holistic view of the individual as a body-mind gestalt has a long history in dance-movement therapy as well (Bernstein, 1979, 1981). Such a perspective is of particular importance when exploring early development of the self and mother-child interaction. "The beginning of the sense of individual identity and separation from the object is mediated by our bodily sensations.

Its core is the body image, which consists of a fairly stabilized and predominantly libidinal cathexis of the body in its central and peripheral parts" (Mahler, 1968, p. 36). Winnicott (1965) and Fairbairn (1976) also concur that the first avenue of integration is via kinesthetic sensation and motility. The initial interpersonal relationship occurs in mutual body contact.

Ontogeny of the Self from an Object Relational Perspective

The first stage of object relations development is based on a part-object relationship with the maternal object, i.e. face, body and the breast. Mother is not yet related to as a whole person. The infant feels omnipotent; when desired, s/he creates the part object or "self-object" as Kohut and Wolf (1978) conceptualize this phenomenon. The early weeks are spent in a state of what Spitz (1965) calls "coenesthetic sensing"--an experience of visceral undifferentiated self-object matrix. Absolute primary narcissism exists at this stage as there is a lack of awareness of the maternal agent (Mahler, 1968, p. 11). Mahler employs the metaphor of a bird in an egg not having been hatched yet into the world of relationships.

Mahler describes the next phase, roughly spanning two and a half to six months, as one in which a dual unity exists. Within this symbiotic orbit normal narcissism, defined as "cathexis of the self-object unit with positive affect value," begins (Blanck and Blanck, 1979, p. 57). Here, differentiation gradually takes place with a body image shift from an interoceptive "belly" focus (Winnicott, 1965) toward a sense of body periphery--a needed requirment for body-ego formation (Mahler). These internal "belly" sensations of fullness or emptiness serve to become the origin of the "feeling of self" around which a "sense of identity" will become established (Greenacre, 1958; Mahler, 1957, 1968; Rose, 1964, 1966). Proprioception places a vital role as well and serves "to convey the first glimmerings of a primitive core of a body self" (Mahler and McDevitt, 1982).

Gradually, the child perceives the "I and not-I" phenomenon (Sullivan, 1953) and eventually comes to realize "I am seen and am reflected back to me by the other." Through this process of reflection the child begins to feel that s/he is genuinely viewed and loved as a separate person. A sense of being--of dimensional existence develops. Mahler terms this "the process of separation and individuation." According to her, it occurs in two sub-phases during the six to thirty month age span. The first sub-phase entitled the "practicing sub-phase," is characterized by active locomotion. The toddler crawls and eventually walks away from mother; and then checks back for a "customs inspection" to ensure mother's presence and love. Here, spatial distance is the mode of practicing actual separation from the object. Through this constructive use of aggression the infant develops a separate sense of self.

Kohut describes the mother-child relationship at this phase as the mirroring self-object characterized by the object's responding to and confirming "the child's innate sense of vigor, greatness and perfection" (Kohut and Wolf, 1978, p. 414).

"Rapprochement," beginning around eighteen months, is the second sub-phase. It can best be described as the child's "wish

for his mother to share with him every new
acquisition of skill and experience" (Mahler,
1968, p. 25). "Look Mommy, look what I can
do!" typifies the child's demand as s/he
seeks reflective approval of growing motility
and productions. Kohut conceptualizes the
object as an idealized parent imago in which
realistic self-esteem, ideals and talents
develop out of the fantasized merging with
the infantile, magical, omnipotent parent
object (Kohut and Wolf, 1978).

Narcissistic formations, serving the
need to maintain mother as providing a "good"
environment for growth, gradually split the
self and object into "good and bad" parts,
i.e. "good self" and "bad self"; "good
object" and "bad object" (Blanck and Blanck,
1979). All of these are eventually
internalized in the final phase of object
constancy. Here there is a developmental
progression from what Winnicott (1971)
characterizes as the child's capacity to be
alone in the presence of the mother to the
capacity to hold the positive object in
memory and experience her continuously
whether she is physically present or not.
Thus, the capacity to care for oneself, to be
a nurturing parent to oneself is evolved.

Body-Movement Object Relationship within the Health Dysfunction Continuum

The foregoing description of the
development of object relations and the sense
of self clearly suggests the importance of
the body-movement relationship between mother
and child.

The presence of a "good enough mother"
within a "facilitating environment" allows
the maturational process to occur and results

in a child who has a realistic, positive
sense of self and a capacity to interact in
the world (Winnicott, 1971). Such a child is
capable of realistic assessments of both good
and bad in self and other (Klein).

As Sutherland (1980) describes it,
Winnicott stresses the need for the primary
maternal preoccupation to be one of
attunement to the child's bodily needs and
rhythms. Winnicott saw holding and handling
as vital elements of the movement
interaction. Holding is reflective of the
mother's capacity to identify with her
offspring and provide needed security. It
serves the necessary integration of
developmental elements. Faulty holding
produces a sense of disintegration--"going to
pieces," feelings of "falling forever," of a
sense that there is nobody to hold the self
together. Pathological feelings of
annihilation and non-existence emerge in such
a clinical picture (Sutherland, 1980,
p. 849). Children and adults seek
compensation through scratching, head
banging, and exposure to intense temperature
and environmental changes. Handling serves
personalization and facilitates the formation
of a psychosomatic gestalt. Faulty handling
produces body-ego splitting and a lack of
experience of the realty of being. Bodily
functions are not experienced as part of
self. Poor muscle tone and coordination, tend
to result (Winnicott, 1971, a, b). Mahler
(1968) describes a paucity of maternal
interest in the child's body in some forms of
early pathology. Fairbairn (1980, 1976)
attributes the development of pathology to a
mother's failure to give the infant an
experience of "being loved for himself."

Kohut (1977) relates multiple possible
causes for maladaptive maternal care, among

them: the child not being viewed as loveable and touchable; the child viewed solely as an extension of the mother's grandiose, narcissistic self; or a mother who over gratified through a prolonged symbiosis followed by absence or rejection. Regardless of the specific etiology, when disturbances occur at a time when the self and object are not separate, i.e. during the symbiotic phase of development, the self view will remain fixated at a narcissistic omnipotent state (Mahler, 1968; Kohut, 1977). At this state objects remain split--either all good or all bad. Typically, rather than view the primary object as bad, resulting in the realization that the mother cannot provide good enough care, the infant will take the "blame" and identify his/her being as bad, worthless and unloveable. A realistic sense of self and ego ideal will be absent. Psychic energy remaining tied to archaic structures will tend to shift the cathexis from self-object to body, resulting in psychosomatic dysfuncton. The longing for reunion with the idealized parent imago predominates and demonstrates itself as a literal bodily experience of fusion with the primary object (Kohut, Mahler, Guntrip). Primitive defenses such as denial, dedifferentiaton and bodily deanimation occur with the most severely disturbed. In these instances, the individual is unable even to differentiate from inanimate objects.

The Theoretical Formulations

Methods of Psychoanalytically Oriented Object Relations Assessment Through Observation of Body Movement

Body movement assessment profiles based on the Laban (1947, 1960) system of notation and analysis have become a generic medium for the modern dance-movement therapist's testing and evaluation of normal and clinical populations from infancy to adulthood (Bartenieff, 1981; Bernstein, 1973 a, 1973 b, 1975 a, 1975 b, 1981). Through the developmental and psychoanalytic work of Judith Kestenberg (1965, 1967 a, 1967 b, 1975, 1977, 1979) the concepts of the effort-shape system have been expanded and correlated to Anna Freud's developmental lines, structural and dynamic points of view and, of particular relevance, to the theories of Mahler and Winnicott. Her work has, in part, been documented through a twenty year longitudinal study of two generations of interaction between mothers and their children (Kestenberg, 1965, 1967; Kestenberg and Sossin, 1979).

Briefly, rhythms of tension flow (alternations between free flow-contraction of agonist muscle systems) and bound flow (contraction of agonist and antagonist muscle systems) serve as an apparatus for biological safety and drive discharge. Free flow, or uninhibited movement, is manifested in conditions of safety while bound flow or tense inhibited movement is present when there is danger to the organism. Sustained bound flow or a continued stressed fight/flight sympathetic response results in tense immobilized limbs and so-called torso body blocks. Too much free flow or feeling of safety places the individual in potential danger if s/he is unable to discriminate among objects in the environment.

Shape flow gives form to these motoric reactions to positive or negative stimuli. It is characterized by the alternation between growing and shrinking during inhalation and exhalation. When the torso grows in shape during free flow the individual's body is in greater contact with the general environment such as when an individual expands in a benign atmosphere or with a nurturing good object. During shrinking, the individual closes off from the environment such as when a person huddles into his/herself during a horrifying experience or around a hostile object.

Shape flow may be bipolar involving a symmetrical global response entailing growing and shrinking in all three dimensional planes. (These are delineated as widening or narrowing in the horizontal plane, lengthening or shortening in the vertical plane, and bulging or hollowing in the sagittal plane.) Or, the flow of body shape may be more discrete and directional in assymetrical, unipolar shape flow such as widening toward another or shortening downward away from a threatening object overhead. The more discrete the response, the more delineated the bridge to and from self and other.

By the same token, shape flow serves the transfer of libidinal and aggressive drive from self to objects during id motoric discharge. Here tension flow rhythms (serving oral sucking and biting, playful ambivalent anal libidinal and anal sadistic defecatory straining movements, urethral libidinal liquid flowing and more sadistic starting and stopping rhythms of bladder control as well as the oedipally related inner genital, phallic and genital motoric rhythmic discharges) are all given form and body shaping to provide a bridge to the object through shape flow. For example, the infant widens assymmetrically in shape flow toward the mother's breast. On a smaller zone specific scale, shrinking in shape occurs during the actual suck phase of the oral rhythm as the mouth provides a vacuum like draw on the nipple. As milk enters the mouth a relaxation-free flow phase occurs and the mouth grows in shape.

Directional shape (movement of an arc-like or spoke-like manner in the horizontal, vertical or saggital direction) correlates with ego based modes of object-related learning and defenses against objects and further extends the dimensions of the body into space. Within the plane of spatial orientation and communication, the child can move his/her arm horizontally sideways across his body to reach and fondle mother's free nipple as s/he sucks on the other. Directional movements upward and downward are associated with the control of weight and gravity. Directional movements forward and backward are associated with temporal aspects (Kestenberg, 1975).

Shaping reflects ego apparatuses for complex object relationships, and on a postural level, correlates with the super ego, ego ideal. Here an individual is not solely related to one or two dimensions as in directional shape but three dimensions.

There is a qualitative difference between a mother's greeting entailing extension of the arms to her child in the forward direction and the contour of her arms and torso around her child in an embrace.

Here shaping is involved entailing the three
dimensions of extension-flexion, external-
internal rotation, and abduction-adduction.
A sense of meaningful holding and handling
exists.

Motoric ego adaptations to space,
weight, and time are called "efforts." Effort
qualities serve to mediate id tension flow
drives, and provide the dynamics which are
infused into object related shaping. For
example, does the mother move directly toward
her child or does she proceed with
indirectness taking in more of the
environment in her adaptation to space? Does
she engage in lightness or strength? Does she
move with acceleration or is she slower in
her adaptation to time?

Attributes of tension flow rhythms,
shape flow, directional shape, shaping and
efforts have affinities for one another, and
when demonstrated can be interpreted
psychodynamically as representing successful
object related adaptation. Mis-matching of
these elements demonstrates intra and inter-
structural conflict between id, ego, and
super-ego. (See Figure 1 for a
developmentally based structural matching of
these body movement parameters.) For example,
a mother may seemingly be holding her infant
in a nurturing manner employing the needed
ego based shaping in her arms and torso; but
if her breathing is not attuned to that of
her infant's through the use of proper id
based tension and shape flow, eg. as with a
held bound torso, then the mother is giving
her infant a double message--one which is
reflective of her own interstructural id-ego
conflict.

ID			EGO			SUPEREGO	
Drive Related:	Object Related:		Drive Adaptation Related:	Object Related:		Punitive Superego:	Ego Ideal:
Tension Flow Rhythms	Symmetrical Shape Flow	Assymmetrical Shape Flow	Effort	Directional Shape	Shaping	Postural (P) Efforts	Postural (P) Shaping
oral libidinal (sucking)	widening	lateral	space: indirect	horizontal: sideways out	horizontal: spreading	space: (P)indirect	horizontal: (P)spreading
oral sadistic (biting; chewing)	narrowing	medial	direct	sideways across	enclosing	(P)direct	(P)enclosing
anal libidinal (twisting, expelling)	lengthening	cephalad	weight: lightness	vertical: upward	vertical: ascending	weight: (P)lightness	vertical: (P)ascending
anal sadistic (straining, expelling)	narrowing	caudal	strength	downward	descending	(P)strength	(P)descending
urethral libidinal (flowing)	bulging	anteriorty	Time: deceleration	Sagittal: forward	Sagittal: advancing	Time: (P)deceleration	Sagittal: (P)advancing
urethral sadistic (starting, stopping)	hollowing	posteriorty	acceleration	backward	retreating	(P)acceleration	(P)retreating

Figure 1. Inter-Structural Matching and Affinities of Effort-Shape. (Abstracted from Bernstein, 1982.)

	0 – 6 months	6 – 9 months	0 – 18 months	18 – 30 months	2½ – 30 months
Object Relations (Mahler)	symbiotic phase	differentiation	separation practicing subphase	individuation rapprochement subphase	object constancy
Playing (Winnicott)	mother & baby merged – mother makes baby's omnipotent fantasies real	maternal object repudiated and reaccepted objectively	playing – being alone in the presence of someone		shared playing – mother introduces own playing for playing together
	sense of trust	sense of being – "I am"		sense of doing – "I can do"	
Psychology of Self (Kohut)	Autoeroticism 0 - 2 months	Primary narcissism transformation appearing as grandiose self and idealized parent imago	Formation of cohesive self transmuting internalizations Mirroring self-object	Idealized parent imago	Nuclear self capable of self esteem, ego ideal and cohesive three-dimensional sense of self
Self Object Organization (Kernberg)	Primary undifferentiated self object	Formulation of good self and separate bad self object.	Self Object differentiation, idealization of maternal object as all good. Good and bad split.		Object constancy integration of good and bad self and object.
Tension Flow Rhythms (ID apparatus for drive discharge)	oral libidinal	oral aggressive	anal libidinal & sadistic	urethral libidinal & sadistic	toward inner & outer genital
Shape Flow (ID apparatus for transfer of impulses from self to object	horizontal widening & narrowing	dominance of unipolar over bipolar shape flow	vertical – lengthening & shortening	sagittal – bulging & hollowing	multi-dimensional shape flow
Efforts – (ego apparatus for adaptation)	spatial pre-efforts: channeling & flexibility		weight pre-efforts: gentleness & vehemence	time pre-efforts: hesitation & suddenness	efforts in space, weight and time
Directional Shape and Shaping (ego apparatus for object relations)	horizontal directional shape		vertical directional shape	sagittal directional shape	complex shaping in horizontal, vertical & sagittal planes
Body-Image	positive affect investment	body differentiation from environment	movement of body through space		toward sexual identity
		body part relationship			

Figure 2. Self, Object Relations, and Body Movement Development. (Abstracted from Bernstein, 1982.)

Figure 2 relates these effort-shape developmentally based motoric apparatuses to the concepts of Mahler, Winnicott, Kohut, Kernberg, and Schilder's body image development. Both tables address the relationship between ego psychology with its emphasis on drive discharge and developmental adaptation, and object relations theory with its focus on the individuation process between the emerging self and other. Thus, in order for each phase of early infant development to be organized, the proper interrelationship between adaptation and the needed object related environment becomes crucial. In subsequent sections the importance of breath flow, body posturing, and movement as a primary communicational and organizational bridge between the self and object will be presented.

Effort-Shape and Its Relation to Mahler's Developmental Phases

Mahler's symbiotic phase of development is characterized in movement by lateral shape flow with a predominance of widening and narrowing in the horizontal plane. As in Fairbairn's premise that "libido is not primarily pleasure-seeking, but object-seeking" (1976, p. 137), shape flow; growing and shrinking, must match free and bound flow respectively in id tension flow libidinal rhythms. The infant grows toward the mother's breast in free flow and shrinks in bound flow.

With differentiation from the object, more bound flow is observed to dominate, particularly in the superficial muscles or body periphery. Increased presence of unipolar or asymmetrical shape flow reflects more discrete adaptations to the object, e.g.

lengthening toward or narrowing away from the primary object. Pathology manifested by weak body boundaries can be observed in dominance of neutral tension and shape flow.

The "practicing" sub-phase of separation and individuation reflects a more sophisticated relation to the object. Directional shape, particularly qualities in the vertical up/down dimension, predominates. Anal libidinal ambivalent and anal sadistic tension flow rhythms have affinity with both lengthening and shortening in uni- and bipolar shape flow.

"Rapprochement" is characterizd by a shift from the vertical to the sagittal dimension. The child "operates" in the world, going forward and wanting mommy to see and approve of all s/he can do.

With object constancy comes a gradual development of the capacity for even more sophisticated object relations. The self and object can be experienced as both good and bad, and the capacity to love and hate others and explore the continuum between these affectual polarities can be observed in the complex use of directional shape and shaping. The degree of affinity or matching between the efforts in space, weight, and time and shaping in the horizontal, vertical, and sagittal planes respectively reflect the degree to which ego adaptations (efforts) serve object relations (shape) and vice versa.

Effort-Shape and Its Relation to the Concepts of Winnicott

Winnicott (1971) has stressed the importance of having a sense of self, of

84

"being," which is required first before playing or the capacity to "do" emerges. Kohut, Fairbairn, Guntrip and Mahler have all stressed the need to be viewed and loved as a separate entity, e.g. "When I look (at mother), I am seen, therefore I exist," (Winnicott, 1971, p. 134). Motorically, what is observed is the capacity for shape flow in three dimensions. Developmentally, body widening corresponds to feelings of omnipotence which occur during normal narcissim. Its antithesis, narrowing, correlates with feelings of being deflated. A continuously narrowed or widened body attitude may both be reflective of a narcissistic personality disorder. The later phenomenon occurs where there is an identification with the omnipotent other.

When the flow between widening and narrowing is balanced through proper attunement of the maternal object, feelings of trust are generated. Within the vertical dimension a balance between torso lengthening and shortening correspond to feelings of stability and of control. Sagitally, torso bulging correlates with feelings of "fullness," of having a self inside. Individuals who remain fixed in narrowed, shortened and hollowed shape flow feel deserted, experience an internal emptiness, and are without a sense of self and object. These individuals often exaggerate peripheral bound flow in order to provide an external body armor and experience themselves as an empty shell changing their somatic behavior to insure others' acceptance of them, seeking in vain to fill the internal void from the absent internalized good object. Fairbairn (1976) writes, "At a deep mental level, taking is emotionally equivalent to amassing bodily contents, and giving is emotionally equivalent to parting with bodily contents.

85

There is an emotional equivalence between mental and bodily contents" (p. 14).

Thus, bipolar shape flow instigated through natural breath flow gives a three dimensionality to the body-image and provides a psychosomatic base to self-object representatives.

Kestenberg has utilized the effort-shape system of movement observation and notation in longitudinal research to study the capacity of mothers to attune themselves to their children's developmentally-based movement patterns. Winnicott (1971) and Sutherland (1980) both emphasize that the primary maternal pre-occupation is her attunement to the child. Proper attunement provides the baby with the needed feeling of creative omnipotence which is the precursor for playing--the transitional space which provides the prototype for all creativity and object relationships (Sutherland, 1980, p. 852).

Kestenberg et al. (1975) writes, "The average new mother learns from her infant and allows the infant to learn from her. When he grows toward her she grows toward him, using free flow and adjusting the degree of tension release in a finely modulated manner. When he shrinks away a bit, she shrinks from him using bound flow evenly to insure that he does not lose hold of the nipple. Through mutual attunement and harmonizing the mother-child couple create the dual unity of the symbiotic relationship which characterizes the incipient oral phase" (p. 199).

Winnicott's concepts of "holding" and the "holding environment" have been explored by Kestenberg (1977). Discussing the body-movement correlates of pathology she writes,

"As indicated by Winnicott (1972), the adult patient does not remember what happened to him in his early infancy. However, the early holding failure becomes embedded in his manner of holding himself and in the ways he resettles to achieve more comfort" (p. 355).

Object Relations in Psychoanalytically Oriented Movement Therapy

Winnicott (1971, 1980) and Sutherland (1980) are strongly concurred with regarding the hypothesis that playing becomes the prototype for the therapy experience both with children and adults. "It is only in playing that the individual--child or adult-- uses his whole personality in creative activity, and it is only in creative activity that he discovers this self" (Sutherland, 1980, p. 852). Playing occurs within an intermediate area--it is a transitional phenomeon which bridges the inner and outer world. Through creative enacted expression the child manipulates the external environment in service of a "sample of dream potential" and cathects the previously unconscious affect on to external objects (Winnicott, 1971). The relationship of play to body-movement is reflected in this quote from Winnicott, "here is a part of the ego that is...founded on body experience" (1971, p. 152).

Creative movement improvisations and unconscious free associational movement are fundamental to dance-movement therapy process (Bernstein, 1980, 1981). As Winnicott (1971) writes, the goal of the therapeutic procedure is, "to afford an opportunity for formless experience and for creating impulses, motor and sensory, which are the stuff of playing and on the basis of playing is built the

whole of man's existence" (p. 75). He
emphasizes "holding and handling" in therapy
as well, and has employed various
transitional environments for body movement
expression in order to "facilitate the
child's innate tendency to inhabit the body,
enjoy body's functions and to accept the
limitation that the skin provides, separating
me from not me" (1965, p. 69).

Thus, movement therapy which employs an
object relations frame of reference focuses
on making the pre-verbal explicit through
expressive re-experiencing and symbolic
enactment within the transitional space of
"playing."

The Role of the Psychoanalytically
Oriented Movement Therapist Within
an Object Relations Perspective

The role of the therapist is
characterized by Guntrip (1971) as one of
being "a real person" for individuals so that
they may be able to experience a positive
sense of their own realness and existence. He
contends that the therapist must understand
and learn how to remedy the "catastrophic
lack of sheer mothering" (p. 187) that
individuals suffering from narcissistic
wounds have experienced. Winnicott sees the
potential for this occurring when the
patient/client and therapist "play" together
in the therapeutic environment in which the
individual is able to build a "host of
meaninful memories" that become the prototype
for healthy object relations.

The therapist, like the "good enough
mother," needs to attune her rhythm and body
attitude to that of the patient/client. "When
mother and baby attune to each other's needs,

empathy develops. A similar process occurs in analysis as well, except that both patient and therapist regress in the service of therapy" (Kestenberg, 1977, p. 344). Thus, a harmonizing of shape flow breathing rhythms is needed in order to facilitate the development of trust and a sense of self in relation to the therapist.

Kohut (1977), in his work with individuals manifesting narcissistic pesonality disorders, focuses on the narcissistic transferences which correspond to fixation in Mahler's transitional period between symbiosis and separation-individuation (p. 220). In describing the clinical picture, Kohut states, "The equilibrium of primary narcissism is disturbed by the unavoidable shortcomings of maternal care, but the child replaces the previous perfection (a) by establishing a grandiose and exhibitionistic image of self: the grandiose self, and (b) by giving over the previous perfection to an admired, omnipotent transitioinal self-object; the idealized parent imago" (p. 25). In cases of the latter dynamic, an "idealizing transference" is constellated; in the former situation, a "mirror transference" is formed. In mirror transference, the more genetically primitive of the two, the patient/client, fixated at the symbiotic phase, experiences the therapist as part of the self and demands from the therapist "an echo and a confirmation of his greatness and an approving response to his exhibitionism" (p. 123). It is "the stage in which the child needs the unqualified acceptance and admiration of his total body-mind-self" (p. 152). The role of the therapist is "to reflect and echo" the patient/client (p. 175). By providing a "therapeutic buffer" and an experiential container the individual is able to re-experience and bring into the reality ego grandiose fantasies with reflective acceptance from the therapist.

Marian Chace's pioneer work in dance therapy with psychotic adults had paralleled Kohut's work with the mirror transference. Empathetic movement reflecting, or attunement through mirroring, is a basic therapeutic technique utilized by all dance therapists that have been trained in her approach (Chaiklin, 1975; Bernstein, 1978). Chace would enter the undifferentiated symbiotic world of the narcissistically wounded adult, and through non-verbal movement reflection she drew even the most isolated into a beginning relationship. In emphathetically adapting her movement to that of the patient, Chace believed that a relationship could begin which "cuts through the isolation of the individual" (Chace, 1975, p. 96). Siegel's (1978) research on the "breathing together" technique has confirmed the facilitating effect that mutual body posturing and breath mirroring has on the psychological developmemt of psychotic and organically disabled children.

The trained movement therapist is equipped to undertake object relations assessment profiles based on body movement observation. Providing an environment for unconscious authentic movement and interactional playing based on movement dramatizations, the pre-verbal and unverbalizable can be remembered, re-experienced and brought into expression within the transitional therapeutic space. The dance-movement therapist is skilled to interpret and reflect back to the individual the phenomena that is being brought into consciousness. This can be done through the utilization of the symbolic container created by the patient/client's unconscious, or by facilitating a bridge from the experience to present behavior with significant objects and eventually to the past maternal environment.

Empathetic, attuned movement-mirroring and therapeutic derivatives of holding and handling which are sensitive to the client's needed developmentally-based tension and shape flow can enable the individual to develop "a host of meaninful memories." In this way the needed transferential object relations for differentiation and eventual object constancy can occur, resulting in the individual's experience of internal fullness, of selfhood, and of the capacity both to love and hate and be both good and bad.

Case Study: Psychoanalytic Object Relations in Movement Therapy*

Roberta was one patient who in her own words so aptly illustrated the dilemma of the borderline patient. "To take any step is like falling into outer space." For the child who has not been adequately held, the journey of separation-individuation is far too traumatic to venture. Roberta, the eldest of three sisters, grew up in a town in New England. Her father worked in a shoe factory and her mother worked as a waitress. She grew up in a world where the horizons were narrow and dreams the work of idle minds. It is difficult for a child to become more than their parents can dream of, and for Roberta this had been a constant struggle. The wonder and awe of this child's world had been so coated over with darkness that imagination, dreams and play became dangerous in themselves. With Roberta, as with many

---

*Written by Arlene Avstreih

91

patients who have suffered early deprivation and impingement, the hostile environment was so deeply internalized that her body became an enemy. Her body was something to beat up and punch into shape rather than love and nurture. Roberta felt trapped in her body. On one hand she felt dead; on the other, she felt bombarded by sensations and pain. She wanted a fluid body with which she could fly, but in reality she did not want a body at all.

Roberta was twenty-five when she began treatment. Though she clearly seemed rather intelligent, her low self-esteem had caused her to consistently work far below her ability.

When Roberta started therapy, she was working as a receptionist in a film company. Though she had the potential to be quite lovely looking, she was rather overweight and took little care with her clothes or hair.

Roberta sought treatment because she felt dead most of the time. She hated her job. In fact, she hated most everything about her life, yet she felt it was impossible to change it in any way. In movement, she depicted her world as a tall grey cylinder which surrounded her, coming to chest height. She was able to see the world outside, but there was no easy way to reach it. The only hope for escape was a magical rescue by a helicopter which could lift her up. This is symbolic of the wish for an omnipotent therapist to save her. It is common in the treatment of borderline patients for the therapist to be either idealized or devalued, depending upon which aspects of the self/object representations are being projected onto the therapist.

Body-Movement Assessment

Roberta became aware of the world too early and too suddenly before being able to internalize any sense of innate wholeness. She used a rigidly held musculature to achieve some sense of intactness and defend against feelings of fragmentation. She was literally "holding on for dear life." Breathing patterns needed to be explored. Roberta's breathing was irregular and shallow, reflecting a lack of a sense of on-goingness. She was often uncomfortable breathing and would rather not focus directly on her breath, fearing that if she thought about breathing, she would stop breathing. Kestenberg (1978) refers to the early breathing patterns of the mother and infant as precursors to the separation-individuation process. The irregular breathing pattern of these patients remind them of the disharmony of the symbiotic experience and accentuates the feelings of separateness and helplessness they experienced at that time.

For a time, Roberta and I worked directly on breathing in order to gain deeper understanding and mastery of issues surrounding her irregular and shallow breathing. Roberta would become very uncomfortable when she would focus on her breath. It became clear that she held her breath to ward off intense feelings of fear and rage. If I placed my hand firmly but gently on her diaphragm, it enabled her to relax and breathe more deeply. My touch served as a container for her intense feelings and provided the sense of ongoing connectedness which was so absent in her initial symbolic experience. Slowly, we were able to work towards dynchronous breathing. We would sit face-to-face on the floor with our hand on each other's chest. In this way

93

we were able to sense the flow of breath.
Here, we were able, in a sense, through our
mutual representativeness, to recreate the
symbiotic attunement and facilitate the
integration of a reliable object.

I had also found that her movements were
not supported by her breath, indicative of
the lack of an internalized holding
environment. Transitions were abrupt or
missing and phrasing was often unclear and
disorganized, again indicative of the early
disharmony.

What was most striking, was that it
seemed that almost no movement, or place in
my office was experienced as comfortable.
Roberta, like other borderlines, was
constantly aware of discomfort; there was no
way to just be in the world. It was not
uncommon to hear comments like, "I hate my
body, I wish I could just cut out my stomach
and get rid of all the bad feelings." For
Roberta, her body reminded her of her life's
original failure; that of being an infant who
could not experience synchrony with her
mother.

Therapeutic Process

It was quite difficult to sustain the
work solely with the images and movements
that Roberta brought into session. In order
to work consistently with such material, a
working alliance needed to develop. A working
alliance is dependent on a degree of basic
trust--the embellishment of which has been
severely impeded in the borderline patient.
Therefore, it was initially impossible for
Roberta to enter into a mutual relationship.
One of the main developmental defects of the
borderline patient is the inability to

integrate libidinal images with primitive aggressive and self-punitive self/object representations. (Meissner, 1981, p. 106) In order to maintain some sort of psychic equilibrium, Roberta employed a predominance of splitting through the use of projections and introjection. In treatment, this, of course, became intensified and she vacillated between idealizing me, thus projecting her own omnipotent self-representations, and devaluing me to ward-off the intense dependency strivings. In either case, she was unable to join in the partnership. Interpretations and interventions were often experienced as critical, as the more aggressive, self-punitive aspects of Roberta's psyche became projected onto me. The more fragmented the early self/object representation, the more they will be split-off onto the therapist. The therapist must be able to contain and integrate immense amounts primitive rage and hate. This is experienced both somatically, as well as psychically. Countertransferentially, the therapist must work through feelings of being bombarded, obliterated and often made to feel helpless and powerless. The management of these primitive feeling states became the essence of her therapy. Slowly, I needed to help Roberta clarify and differentiate reality from her world of projected self/object representations. In the process of therapy, I work towards the integration of her libidinal and aggressive introjects in order to neutralize her aggression and free this psychic energy for ego adaptation.

As the transference unfolded, Roberta experienced times of great reluctance to move. The projection of her own intense rage would severely distort her reality testing and it was not uncommon for her to feel that I was on the verge of attacking her. The therapist must be on guard against the possibility of a psychotic transference when projective identification so severely disrupts reality testing. It does not help to merely reassure the patient that you are not how they perceive you to be. The basic trust is too distorted to internalize the more benign introject without working through in depth the critical introject which has been activated.

The splitting process was constantly evident in the treatment. Borderlines live in a world of extremes which is manifested in their movement. Either Roberta was in a state of collapse or intense rigidity. I was either a "softie" or a "bitch". It was impossible for her to experience me as both warm and strong. When she would perceive me as strong, it would destroy previous perceptions of my warmth and nurturance, and I was accused of being a "phony".

Once as we were working on grounding and walking, Roberta had an extremely negative reaction. In Roberta's world, to be grounded meant to be glued to one spot. The floor took on the negative aspects of the maternal introject which forbid exploration and demanded almost complete relinquishment of autonomy. I suggested to Roberta that she think of the floor as something which she could leave and return to. This freed her to use her legs with strength and jump quite high with a sense of pleasure. The intervention allowed her to exprerience the floor as the reliable mother who encouraged exploration but was there when needed.

Each time we would work together some of the aggressive and self-punitive introjects, Roberta could begin to expand her exploration of the world. Eventually, she left her job as

a receptionist and took a training position
in a large firm which offered good benefits
and some possibilities for advancement. She
lost weight and changed her hair style,
becoming more and more attractive. Each
assertion, each step was met with intense
feelings of guilt and fear of retaliation.
This was again projected onto the therapist
who Roberta was sure would hate her for every
possible step she made. Again, she was dealt
with not by reassurance but by exploration of
the projections thereby eliciting the
observing ego in the therapeutic process.

As the therapeutic alliance developed
and the trust in the therapist grew, Roberta
began to become more and more depressed. The
core abandonment depression began to surface.
This is a very crucial aspect of the therapy.
As the patient begins to experience the
positive, growing relationship with the
therapist, the full depth of the deprivation
and abandonment is felt for the first time.
The pain is immense and the possibility of
suicide can be real. It is in this stage of
the therapy that the patient has the
opportunity to learn about love and
compassion. In this stage of the treatment,
Roberta had a dream about a monkey. In the
dream, the monkey was asking for food.
Roberta didn't want to be bothered feeding it
so she left and closed the door. A short time
later, she returned. When she opened the
door, she saw the monkey, holding a baby
monkey in her arms, reaching up towards
Roberta, begging for food for her baby.
Though this dream can be looked at on many
levels, one of the significant aspects of
this point in the treatment was the
recognition of the starving baby-self who
needs to be fed. As Roberta began to work
through this depression, she gradually became
aware of her own deeply repressed needs. She

began to realize how isolated she was and how
much she wanted friends with whom she could
share and depend. As a child, she had loved
to paint. She began to take art courses; and
as she progressed, it became quite apparent
that she had some real talent. For one of her
assignments, she decided to do a series of
self-portraits. She would come to sessions
with a sketch pad and a record. First she
would dance and then she would draw. Slowly,
she began to create herself in my presence.

Her early dances were small. She finally
dared to abandon her omnipotent desire to fly
and allowed herself to experience the small,
helpless child within. She would curl up on
the floor and allow her movements to unfold
gently and slowly. Initially, she worked a
lot with space/flow as she slowly began to
move from inside to outside. I was very
careful not to push her exploration but to
allow her to explore at her pace and in her
way. She literally discovered or re-
discovered her body parts. She spent months
working with her legs; feeling them,
stretching, standing, walking, running,
jumping and finally leaping. She could now
experience her legs as strong and able to
support her. She drew beautiful portraits of
herself running and leaping through fields.
She used bold lines and vibrant colors
symbolizing her growing sense of identity and
energy.

As her interest in art grew, she decided
to investigate pursuing a degree in Art
Education. As fate would have it, she was
accepted to a very fine school out of town.
Although we both agreed that she still had
some important work to do in therapy, we also
felt that her pursuit of her education and
all that it represented to her was very
important at this time. We worked hard on the

termination. I still hear from Roberta. She is doing well in school and has started therapy again which continues to support her growth.

Conclusion

In a healthy relationship, the infant exists apart from the needs and projections of the mother. By working with the transference, the therapist is able to recreate this holding environment. As the therapist becomes more and more free from the projected distortions of the patient, she/he can be internalized as a reliable, supportive object; one who encourages authenticity and exploration.

The movement therapist is able to encourage growth and authenticity on the original body level. Authentic movement allows for the uninterrupted experience of being so essential for a sense of self. Through authentic movement the client can experience impulses and sensations free from impingement and external stimuli. Winnicott (1965b) would refer to this as an Id Experience.

"In the course of time there arrives a sensation or an impulse. In this setting the sensation or impulse will feel real and be a truly personal experience. ...A large number of such experiences form the basis for a life that has reality instead of futility" (p. 35).

The body is the dwelling place of the self. By being able to work with both the body and the mental representations, the dance therapist can facilitate a psychosomatic integration which is the wellspring of a true feeling of wholeness.

99

**Theoretical Model: Object Relations Theory
within a Jungian Analytic Perspective**

Concepts

View of the Individual

The individual is seen as an organismic
unity of soma and psyche whose individuated
uniqueness emerges into consciousness from an
"a priori unconscious existence" (Jung, CW6
p. 112). The only way to experience
unconscious phenomena directly is through the
somatic unconscious (Schwartz, 1983). The
appreciation of the nature and meaning of the
somatic unconscious is figural in the
psychology of Jungian movement therapy.
Classic psychoanalysis views the unconscious
as predominantly a receptacle of repressed
dreams and traumas. This is delineated as the
personal unconscious in analytic work. There
is, however, a deeper layer or collective
unconscious which is inborn. It is called
"collective" because of the universality of
its contents and themes of behavior. It is
thus a "common psychic substrate of a
suprapersonal nature which is present in
everyone" in all times and cultures (Jung
CW9, p. 4). The contents of these two strata
of the unconscious clearly differ. In the
personal, the feeling-toned experientially
acquired layer of complexes are present. In
the collective unconscious or objective
psyche, the contents are known as archetypes.

Archetypes are premordial and universal.
They may be symbols, thematic mythelogems or
body movements. They are readily apparent in
their projected externalization of the gods
and goddesses individuals have worshipped
from Isis to Christ; the myths and fairy
tales people have told from Beowolf and the

Odyssey to Horatio Alger and Star Wars; and
the movements and bodily attitudes
individuals have embodied from the rhythmic
pelvic undulations of puberty rites to the
circle and square mandalas in folk dances.

These archetypal images are, however,
"first and foremost psychic phenomena that
reveal the nature of the soul" (Jung, CW9,
p. 6). They serve to shake loose the
underpinnings of the complexes of the
personal unconscious thus allowing
individuals a deep conscious connection to
the mystery and meaning of life and their
fundamental relationship to all of humanity.

The Ontogeny of Consciousness and Relationship to the Self

Edinger (1972) writes, "We are born in a
state of inflation. In earliest infancy
neither ego nor consciousness exists" (p. 7).
This is union with the gods or paradise
before the expulsion.

The development of consciousness and
selfhood in an individual begins first in a
uroboric-pleromatic stage in which the
unhatched fetal infant or body-self as
Neumann (1973) characterized it is overlaid
by the mother's self. Here the ego is
embedded in the archetypal unconscious. Thus
the infant experiences the personal mother as
the omnipotent archetypal Great Mother. The
symbol of the uroboros is one of a circular
snake eating its tail and is characteristic
of the dynamic of "oppositionless unity of
psychic reality" (p. 10).

This phase is soon replaced by the First
Matriarchal Phase: The Post-natal Embryonic
phase which parallels Mahler's symbiotic

101

state (roughly three weeks to six months).
Here there is a continued sense of a merged
unitary self with the mother. The ego-self
remains dormant in the uroboros which is
experienced physically. There is a
participation mystique which exists between
the matriarchate and the infant. Everything
is shared, merged. Since the self is
externalized in the object, mother's
psychology, manifested through her
unconscious movement patterns, is blended
with that of the infant's.

The beginning of the separation
individuating processes of Mahler's is
heralded by the Second Matriarchal Phase in
which there occurs a process of separation of
World Parents. Here the polarization of good
and bad self and object begins to develop.
The personal mother will either constellate
the positive good nurturing-creating mother
archetype and/or the terrible devouring or
abandoning mother archetype. With the latter,
infants frequently become polarized as a bad
ugly-unworthy greedy monster. Even when the
object provides good enough nurturing,
however, a natural depressive position
develops when the baby begins to experience
the mother as a whole object.

Analyst Fordham (1969) writes,

"The change from part to whole object
relation is especially significant
because it means that objects previously
felt to be either good or bad,
blissfully satisfactory or
catastrophically frustrating and
persecuting, can now be recognized as
the same object. Consequently, the baby
becomes concerned, lest, in his angry or
greedy attacks, he damages or destroys
his mother's good breast when he feels

it is bad. And he can now feel that this
has happened and recognize his need for
his mother's continued existence"
(p. 121).

With a developing capacity for mobility,
the toddler's ego functions are being
developed in relation to doing. Thus the
participation mystique as Jung denoted it is
gradually diminishing. This stage culminates
in what Fordham identifies as "unit status."
It is characterized by the appreciation of
self as a separate entity capable of engaging
in internal activity with a developed
positive mother complex. This complex is
composed of a host of significant bodily
engagements with the personal mother as well
as the constellated images, themes, and
movements of the mother archetype.

The ego and other complexes will
continue to develop toward a more
individuated relationship to the Self--the
universal archetype of individuation and
wholeness. Because of the appreciation and
valuing of the objective psyche and the need
for a mature conscious relationship to it,
Jungian analysts have viewed the
individuation process as continuous, with the
first half of life spent separating the ego
from the Self and the second half providing a
dynamic ego-Self axis. Ego Psychologist Erik
Erikson (1963) came closest to this model
with his "Eight Stages of Man," but because
of the empirical reductionistic view of the
unconsious and the overvaluing of the ego,
the relationship to the collective
unconscious and its archetypal contents were
never sufficiently addressed. Jungians view
the ego as "the seat of subjective identity,
while the Self is the seat of objective
identity" (Edinger, 1972, p. 3).

Given a Jungian perspective, it is therefore imperative to understand the connection to the objective psyche, and from an analytic object relational perspective to reflect on the continuing evolution of the ego, Self and mother complexes.

At this point, however, it is imperative to provide a dual focus: both on the psychology of men and the animus (the complex in women from which is constellated their relationship to their musculine nature) and the psychology of women and the anima (the complex in men from which their relationship to the feminine is constellated).

From thirty months to roughly four years, the Chthonian Stage of consciousness is dominant in which ego activities are dependent on bodily experiences and thus under the rule of the Mother archetype. Both inner genital and phallic movements dominate. With the former, the bodily experience is internal. These wave like contractions with gradual ascent and descent of tension flow are associated with the "unseeable" unconscious. The intrusive phallic ballistic movements with their jumps, leaps, stabbing, kicking and eventually punching provide externalized discharge. The symbolic material of children's fantasies, adult dreams and authentic movement experiences related to this phase are associated with instinct and lie within the realm of the mother complex. Monsters, ghosts, dragons, primordial sea creatures, and other figures of the feminine associated with water and earthy underworld can emerge.

From four to five and a half, the Oedipal/Electra Magic Warlike and Magical Creative Stages develop. For the female anima, themes of being rescued from an instinctual beast (father) emerge. Eventually the beast needs to be transformed in some way so that an unconscious symbolic incestual relationship with the father complex can develop out of this universal mythelogem and an initial crystallization of the animus in the woman can occur.

For the masculine ego and animus, the dragon mother complex with its connection to the unconscious needs to be slayed as with Beowulf, Siegfried and St. George. The male ego is frequently swallowed up in a kind of puer (boy) attachment to the mother, like Jonah and the Whale. In the end, however, the masculine ego-animus eventually opposes the mother. "The Oediple conflict strongly reinforces the establishment of anima and animus figures which lie ready as it were to be projected in the love relationships of adolescence" (Fordham, 1969, p. 129).

During latency the father complex replaces the mother as super ego. The persona differentiates and social interest develops. Boys are encouraged in sports (war games) and the values of reason, linear perspective, consciousness, authority of society, logos, and competition are stressed.

In the traditional Western patriarchal society in which most women, and therefore men's animas, have been raised, the development of feminine consciousness has been subtly, but nonetheless strongly repressed. This repression begins to emerge in force during the latency period.

Neumann (unpublished) writes, "The negative consequences of the 'patriarchate' for the woman thus form a vicious circle, in which the man confines the woman to the domain of the merely feminine and thereby makes any real share in the patriarchal culture impossible for her, crowding her into the role of the second rate and the inferior" (p. 28-29). Although societal modes and externalized forums can be suppressive, the collective unconscious is autonomous and unindividuated contents--in this case a valuing and experience of the feminie-- contiunues to emerge in its unconscious darker aspects until it is consciously received.

Whitmont (1982) writes, "Women have an ego which is indeed feminine" (p. 84); and embodied dream material and authentic movement experiences clearly support this premise.

In the past when the feminine was valued, little girls would be taught the significance of the cyclic flow of the eternal round of creating and destroying, of death and rebirth, of intuition, receptivity, embodied instinct and communal society. Priestesses of Artemis, Greek goddess of the hunt and moon, would take young latency girls into the wilderness to explore and be at one with nature.

Neumann's "self-preservation" phase of feminine development in which the feminine ego is bound to the "motherly unconscious" and to the Self may have phase appropriate relevance here. For at this age the girl naturally remains both societally and psychologically tied to the "mother clan."

Clearly the development of an androgenous perspective, however, with values which encompassed a continuum between the matriarchal and patriarchal polarities would be the most appropriate means of affording children the understanding of the choices available.

During puberty, the development of consciousness is divided between the Solar Warlike Phase for the animus/male ego and the Lunar Cyclic Phase for the anima/female ego. In the latter, power is based on an embodied connection to the creative dark womb, whereas the masculine view bases its power in the connection to the light localized symbolically with the head and eye of rational thought. In the female puberty ritual, there is a search for an experience of the feminine source: usually thematically characterized by a descent and sacrifice and a surrender to retrieve feminine wisdom in an embodied way. The Innana myth described by Perera (1981) is such a journey. For the solar warlike animus or pubescent male, the puberty ritual entails a search for mastery over the body, unconsciousness, instinct and fears. Boys are sent alone into the wilderness and then are initiated into the spiritual mysteries of manhood. Whitmont (1982) writes, "As the reasoning light of the mind grasps the world in its outer, concrete manifestation, the inner gnosis, with its magical, instinctual attunement to fundamental survival needs and collective dynamics is lost to consciousness. The world of the Feminine, of the Goddess and her consort Dionysis or Pan, yields to...the Father in heaven whose place eventually is usurped by the now defined reasoning I" (p. 68).

During adolescent for the male ego/animus there can occur a gradual questioning of the primary reality of the ego and the continued employment of secondary personalization (the reduction of the archetypal to personal) in the Solar

Rational. Not everyone wrestles with this, however, as Maslow (1954) finally recognized. Not everyone has a self-actualizing psychology. Some are caught in the initial battle and never move beyond. These are the adolescents who continually rebel against parental values in a desire to achieve selfhood separate from both the external parent and internal complexes. Others separate only to become clones of their parents in later years. In others the feminine ego/anima remains polarizd in the use of the Lunar Intuitive. For some, however, the desire to individuate is not based on peer norms, but a deep inner connection to a quest toward wholeness.

This is the journey of the hero and heroine. In the first stage, the anima and animus are fully crystalized from the mother and father complexes respectively. The male receives his soul anima and the female, an eros connection to a spiritual guide. Both culminate in a hieros gamos or coniunctio-- often symbolized as a sexual union of the masculine and feminine aspects of the individual.

During the second stage which begins in adulthood (usually mid-thirties), the heroic and heronic quest matures toward completion. If the man is unable to reintegrate and reclaim his anima, he becomes "souless," moody and temperamental, and if the woman remains subject to anumus possession, she continues to experience the regressive pull of the terrible mother. In this stage both male and female confront each other and reclaim their anima and animus projections onto each other.

For the male, the quest continues with symbolic death, descent into the underworld

(cave, water, earth), and mutilation or
dismemberment culminating in a resurrection
and rebirth. Archetypal figure such as
Osiris, Dionysus and Christ typify this
journey.

In the female quest, the woman/anima
frequently experiences being raped by her
deeper unconscious--impregnated by an
individuating potential. She enters what
Neumann termed the "Paternal uroboros" in
which the archetypcal Great Father emerges.
"She is seized and laid hold of by a
'powerful penetration' that is not
personally related to a concrete male but is
experienced as an anonymous transpersonal
Numen." (unpublished, p. 13). In figure 3,
Zues comes down as a cloud from the heavens
and unites with Io. Rage, grief, loss, and
waiting culminate in an abandonment and self-
surrender to her own instinct as embodied and
moving through her. In this way spiritual
penetration combines with body-felt
experince. "This means that she understands
symbolically speaking, not with the head but
with the whole body and spiritual and
corporal processes in her are bound together
in a way quite foreign to the average man"
(Neumann, unpublished, p. 15).

If caught in an incompletion of this
phase, the woman would be tied to the
paternal uroborus and lose her relation to
her embodied feminine soul. She might become
a nun to a spiritual father guru or be an
"anima woman" for men's projections. But if
she continues the journey, s/he is ripened
with the pregnancy of her Self. Neumann's
self-finding or highest phase of feminine
development characterizes this final stage of
the individuation quest. Woman is thus reborn
from the Great Mother archetype, as Sophia
and, related to the feminine self, she

becomes wholly a virgin unto her Self"
(Harding, 1971; Hall, 1980; Neumann 1973).

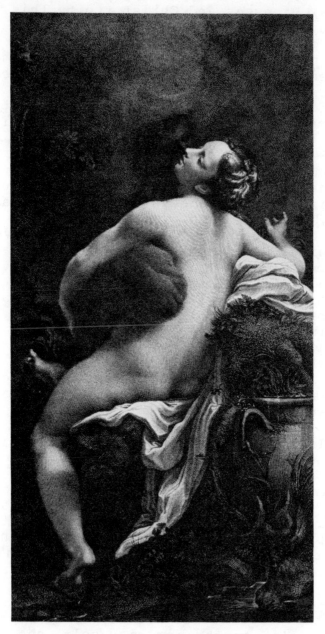

Figure 3. Zeus and Io.

The Eleusian mystery rites of Demeter
and Persephone provide one of the most
powerful prototypes for this journey.
Persephone sought to know deeply and was
caught in the chthonic paternal uroborus,
raped by the underworld, and brought through
chaos to death. Her mother Demeter rages for
her and after sufficient suffering, she Self-
surrenders. Persephone, symbolizing her
embodied unique Self, ascends and is Self-
found and reunited with her. See figure 4.

The result with both quests is a shfit
of the egocentric ego with its personalistic
view of how the world can provide its needs,
to a relationship to the Self. With this
continuing experience there is an
understanding of the "total picture" and of
the deeper significance of one's individual
life in relation to the whole and the
eternal.

Theoretical Formulations

The Health Dysfunction Continuum and Methods
of Analytic Object Relations Assessment in
Body Movement

Pathology can emerge at any stage and is
manifested in the individuating
somatizations, projections on to the world
and one sided behavior typically based on the
overdominant relationship of one polarized
complex.

In analytic work, assessment is also
made through access to the contents of the
unconscious via dreams, authentic movement
and other forms of active imagination.

	Male/Animus	Female/Anima
0 - 3 weeks	Uroboric - Pleromatic Stage	
3 weeks - 6 months	First Matriarchal Stage: The Post-Natal Embryonic Phase	
6 months - 2½ years	Second Matriarchal Stage: The Separation of World Parents	
2½ years - 4½ years	Chthonian Stages Inner and Outer Genital Phases	
4½ years - Latency	Male/Animus Magic Warlike Stage	Female/Anima Magic Creative Stage
Puberty	Solar Warlike Phase	Lunar Cyclic Phase
Adolescence - Adulthood	Solar Rational	Lunar Intuitive
Young Adulthood	Heroic Quest: Hieros Gamos	Heroinic Quest Hieros Gamos
Advanced Adulthood	Heroic Quest: Ego-Self Axis	Heroinic Quest: Ego-Self Axis

Figure 4. Ontogeny of the Consciousness of Self.

Pathology emerges when the external environment does not provide the needed atmosphere for the development of consciousness and a relationshp to the Self. In the early development of object relations, a mother's inability to provide a pleromatic environment for a participation mystique in which self and object are one, produces all the body-movement phenomena described earlier in the psychoanalytic view of the health dysfunction continuum. What is added to the methods of assessment is an interest in and valuing of the way in which the unconscious through its symbolism and archetypal mythic journeys, reveals the psychic condition and guides the client and therapist in the individuation process.

Archetypal and Mythic Themes in Body Movement Assessment

Complexes

Personified numinous collective energy forms the archetypal core of complexes. They emerge as split off portions of the psyche, which are surrounded by experiences and affect-ridded associations to personal phenomena. In the father complex, for example, the archetypal Great Father is symbolically imaged and experienced as, say, Yahweh--The Father God of the Old Testament. In pathological situations Yahweh is imprisoned by the individual's negative experiences with the actual personal father, resulting in the individual having access to only the negative aspects of the transpersonal father.

Proper relationship to this complex means that access to the multiple and dual natures of the Great Father archetype would be available. This connection to the numinous allows for a flow of wisdom from a collective pool of knowing which can afford potential availability of healing and psychic transformation.

To do justice to the infinite amount of archetypal manifestations in complexes would be impossible and not appropriate for the focus of this chapter. Thus those complexes which are typically relevant in the development of object relations will be focused upon along with their body-movement manifestations.

Mother Complex

If the individual's personal mother is unable to provide a facilitating environment of good enough bodily mirroring and attunement, the archetype of the Great Mother will be surrounded by an ever increasing compilation of negative experiences with the original object and thus become unaccessible to the individual. Frequently, a darker polarized portion of the mother archetype is only available to the individual. As with Kali, who on the one side of her perpetually gives birth to human kind and on the other devours, the Great Mother archetype in her dual nature manifests both the creative and destroying aspects of the life cycle. With a negative object, only the poisoning, suffocating, devouring, destructive side of the archetype has any potential of being constellated.

Somatically what is frequently observed is a physical hunger and abdominal emptiness. The therapist countertransferentially may somatically experience being devoured by the hungry infant-child or feel the need to suckle the individual. Caught in the idealized transference, the therapist may experience him/herself as "brilliantly solar and godlike with his/her ideas or instinctually mystically healing with her embodied suggestions." Frequently, clients describe somatic images of great bottomless caves and maws which emerge in the torso area. Negative female figures take shape from the unconscious and can be experienced in active imagination authentic movement and embodied dreams. She becomes the overpowering ocean and the personification of death with its sarcophagus and underworld. On a Chthonic thermiomorphic level, snakes, dragons, and any large devouring water creatures such as sharks or whales can represent aspects of her nature. She is Medusa with snake hair, dark witches and wicked stepmothers.

In one authentic movement experience, a woman found herself to be enveloped by a sphinx-like creature who clawed at her. In another, the clinet continually experienced a Medusaesque figure whose glare resulted in freezing the child self. In this state the client remained frozen in a supine position-- unable to move.

Transferentially, one schizophrenic patient complained that every time I moved or spoke, she felt that she disappeared. Physical spacing in the room and my continued verbal and nonverbal silence was the only avenue open to her experience of me as a safe container--one that did not devour her fragile undifferentiated ego.

Once the positive aspect of the object is constellated in the transference, other symbolic manifestations emerge. Graves turn into safe wombs; and caves open into gardens, rich forests, fields of ripened crops; and stormy, enveloping oceans turn into placid lakes, wells, and fertile swamps. Helpful animals such as cows and rabbits take the place of devouring, entwining, and poisonous beasts; and the great nurturing Earth Mother replaces the dark witches of the Terrible Mother. In one dramatic movement experience, a man reclaims his heart from a wise old woman. In another, a woman experiences drifting in a pristine lake. When she reached its center, she feels her body being cradled and a voice saying to her that she will be with her always. Another woman frolics with her dog, another with a floppy eared maternal rabbit.

Transferentially, the client may ask to be held or may wish to rest and merge quietly in the accepting plermatic uroboric atmosphere of the therapy container. S/he may offer parts of the body to be touched-- related to, cared for or s/he may engage in a rebirthing utilizing the therapy space as a womb and the therapist as good mother.

Transformation can be observed when the movement transitions become softened and rounded with libidinal inner genital tension flow. Bodily shaping with archetypcal feminine movement patterns such as gathering and scattering and those found in the feminine patterns of Laban's space harmony scales emerge. Archetypal enactments of planting and tending gardens, giving births, making vessels, and getting water from springs have been reported. Kundalini like experiences with Shakti, the feminine creative force in yoga, have also occurred in which numinous energy fills the body and aids in physical transformation within the individuation process (Bernstein, 1981).

Animus and Anima Complexes

A woman's relationship to her masculine nature is personified in the animus, and a man's relation to his feminine aspect is experienced as his anima. Both remain undifferentiated in the early months of object internalization in their respective same sex parental figures, i.e. the animus within the father complex and the anima within the mother complex. Real differentiation emerges gradually through various stages of crystallization beginning in the magic warlike/magic creative stages and culminating in adolescence and early adulthood with the hieros gamos or marriage of the contrasexual aspects of the individual's psychology.

The animus in women frequently represents the hero archetype who is capable of shedding the light of consciousness onto the richness of the feminine, awakening this deep source of unconscious wisdom and creativity like the princes in Sleeping Beauty and Snow White. But in narcissistic wounds where the ego is still dominated by the mother complex, the animus too has no choice but to be constellated in relationship to the negative mother as well. In her service, he swears to protect the vulnerable self from the onslaught of an original unsafe environment and to ensure that no one "gets in" to see how bad or how blungeoned this wounded self really is. Frequently, the animus takes on aspects of Winnicott's split off false self (1971a).

The anima in men, never having sufficiently crystalized from the mother complex, remains maudlin and depressed like Rapunzel locked up in the castle of the wicked witch mother. Unable to extricate his

his own feminine nature and relate to her in a mature coniunctio, he remains forever a wounded puer, the mother's boy. He is unable to commit himself to external women, for none can complete with his negative anima-mother complex. The puer aeturnus possessed by this complex typically manifests a false self narcissistic grandiosity toward others to compensate for his inner experience of an inferior bad self.

On a body movement level, an animus possession manifests itself in a saggital body attitude and directional shape. Quickness and directness with urethral sadistic tension flow can be observed in women who embody their animus in life and in particular during active imagination movement experiences. Here, sharp angular transitions are choreographed with rigid shaping, and life is reduced to what "needs to be done" carried out in an abrupt but ordered manner.

Transformation occurs when the sharp angles and compulsive doing is softened and brought into proper balance with her feminine nature. Her capacity to be in the authentic movement frequently manifests in more anal and urethral libidinal tension flow. Imageful numinous experiences of a positive archetypal figure are cathected and experienced. The archetype may be a new individuated animus figure or it may be a new eros aspect of her feminine nature now available to relate to and help transform the animus. Here is where experiences of coniunctio occur in which women report having been penetrated by light or some other archetypal aspect of the masculine. At this point, her feminine nature would have to have been sufficiently crystalized out of the mother complex to surrender to this hieros gamos.

For the man with an anima possession, his body movements may lack shoulder strength. He may have difficulty getting into a standing position and moving through the space in the room as his negative anima would be busy maintaining him in an imprisoned depressed state telling him he cannot create.

When a man has not sufficiently gone through a healthy separation-indiviuation process from the mother and thus suffers from a narcissistic wounding, his puer (boy) complex will also be affected in relation to his anima. Here, the opposite movement enactments become apparent. As the inflated puer, the male client can be seen literally flying through the movement space. Soaring with his own ungrounded inflation with the anima by his side.

In situations with a female therapist, in which the anima rather than the typical mother complex is transferred, the male client may seek an eros connection and dream of "dancing with" the mysterious priestess archetype.

Persona Complex

The persona typically begins to develop during latency. With self pathology, however, it is rendered undifferentiated and under the power of the negative mother complex. Ordinarily this collective facade represents a "compromise between the individual and society as to what a wo/man should appear to be" (Jung, from Singer, 1973, p. 210). In the case of a narcissistically wounded individual, this compromise becomes heavily skewed. The individual does his/her best to serve what would please the other and acts accordingly.

Smiling or mask-like bound faces, latest clothing styles, and societal peer behavior are layered on. The persona becomes adept at mirroring others back to themselves serving as both projection and as a means of providing needed acceptance from the external world.

Active imagination work with mask making and dramatic movement enactments have produced masks with mirrors ("I am a reflection of you") originally evolved to serve the narcissistic mother (Bernstein, 1982). Other masks look bland, innocent, sweetly childlike or clownish on the outside while the inside is painted teary-eyed or red with anger and bloody from wounds.

When moved out in relation to others, these dramatic enactments provide potent embodiments of a split between the persona complex and the Self.

Transformation of the persona complex is frequently observed in the level at which the client is willing to let go of ego control in relation to authentic movement experiences. Issues such as--are the movements that emerge aesthetically pleasing, "authentic" enough or will the therapist find out about the inner me--drift by the wayside as s/he can experience surrendering to the "nakedness" of the process.

Shadow Complex

The shadow typically represents same-sex unindividuated aspects of men and women. They may be positive and/or negative qualities. With insufficient object relations, the negative bad monster self aspects eventually emerge in all its chthonic thermiomorphic manifestations followed by the unconscious positive aspects of the masculine and feminine nature of men and women respectively.

When the transferential container develops sufficiently the narcissistically wounded client is able to embody the wounded self. When these mutant, distorted, deformed, sub-human creatures are finally shown to the caring therapist, the wounds can begin to be healed and the slow but sure transformation of the bad self into a beautiful infant can take place.

At these times, touching and holding can be a powerful catalyst in the therapy as it allows for a re-creation of the mother child uroboros. Synchronistic mirroring of breath flow has a subtle but profound effect on the environmental creation of the mirroring transference. Body boundaries subside as the rich pleromatic energy fills the therapy container. Physical tingling is felt in the body periphery, belly, mouth, and/or hands which are frequently met with the client's fears of fragmentation, dependency, and erotic union.

As the body image homuncular distortions are encouraged to live, the individual's wounded self will come forth. Hairy and beast-like, arms, hands and particularly bellies and mouths are felt to enlarge and dominate sensory awareness. Countertransferentially, the therapist somatically experiences either the physical fragmentation of the merger and infusion into the client or being devoured by eyes which remain fixed on the therapist's eyes which see and fill the client with selfhood.

With other clients, the wounded false self will greet the therapist. Here a composite of introjected reactions of impingement on the natal self produce a shell like defensive barrier. In these cases, the size and philogenic development of teeth are distorted. Body periphery is felt as tense, bristly, prickly like a porcupine.

Angry monster selves emerge with these individuals. They may need a soft but firm container to enact this "bad" self or a mirroring in body movement. At times, these angry monster selves may be deeply relieved to find another accepting "angry monster" to match growls and swipes with gnarled claws. Typically in squatting positions with a firm broad stance, the monster confrontation can develop into trickster playfulness or a mutual respectful stand off.

Ego Complex

Unlike classic Freudian and neo-Freudian depth psychological approaches, the ego is not the most central dynamic constellation within an individual's psychology. That position is taken by the Self which will be discussed in the next section. The ego does, however, maintain the role as a mediator and functions best when it is in proper relationship to the Self as its source of consciounsess. When this occurs, a "conscious dialogue" between the ego and the various archetypal symbolic manifestations can develop. "The symbol is then able to perform its proper function as releaser and transformer of psychic energy with full participation of conscious understanding" (Edinger, 1972, p. 110).

When there is early wounding to the narcissistic core, however, the ego-Self axis is not able to develop sufficienlty. The underdeveloped ego frequently remains under the power of the negative mother complex and vacillates between assisting in the protection of the wounded self along with the personal, animus/a, and shadow or overcompensating for a negative self experience through a grandiose exhibitionistic identification with the Self.

Edinger (1972) writes concerning the negative inflated ego, "Too much humility as well as too much power striving and selfishness, are all symptoms of inflation" (p. 15).

These individuals freuently have difficulty maintaining the needed connection to the moment in order to surrender to authentic movement.

The ego demonstrates its somatic pathology in relation to body shaping and efforts (discussed earlier in the psychoanalytic movement assessment section). The symbolic movement which constellates in the grandiose state is frequently an embodiment of the archetype "Zeus," the great god who emerges at a meeting to give his co-workers the "word." He seems to fill the room with his presence, expansive gestures and body shaping. No one is allowed to outshine him. One may recall that Zeus was an angry god and his potential rage would destroy any mortal who dared his power. Aphrodite, goddess of beauty, might appear in the therapy room. She is frequently impeccably dressed--always in the height of fashion, often fully made up and bedecked with jewelry. No other woman can outshine her without feeling her envy and jealousy.

(Remember what happened to Psyche when mortal men begin to praise her beauty over Aphrodite's.) Finally, Narcissis, from whom this wound has received its name, is frequently embodied. Here can be seen a puer, caught in a painful dilemma of Self-love, without a sense of individuated selfhood.

Von Franz (1970) describes this puer inflation, "The one thing dreaded throughout by such a type of man is to be bound to anything whatever. There is a terrific fear of being pinned down, of entering space and time completely and of being the one human being that one is" (p. 2).

One male client continuously brought in his dreams already "gestalted"claiming he had already "moved through" his dynamics and inner aspects of himself. He would have dreams of flying too high. Pinning him down to the moment to moment experience of his deep inner agony, loneliness, and longing came only when we shared the same container and only through a continued countertransferentially embodied reflection of his pain.

Self

The Self is the archetypcal symbol of wholeness--the unification of opposites in dynamic balance. Ontogenically, it is the exprience of the totality of the body which first constellates this archetype. Thus the experience of the body as a whole is a sine qua non for the experience of the Self.

The Self is also constellated in various levels of symbolism. Theriomorphically, the horse, snake, bear and elephant are all instinctual Self symbols. One woman's

connection to the weighty prodding
massiveness of herself as an elephant
assisted her in a beginning understanding of
her disconnection with her inner world.

Another, after a long authentic movement
experience, felt herself transform into a
lotus. Another emerged as a rose. The
proceeding case describes the embodied
personification of a massive, yet graceful,
tree.

The classic manifestation of the Self
has been the mandala in circular or quadrant
form.

Anyone who has worked with groups in
dance therapy who has utilized the circle
knows what a unifying effect if has on the
group and what power of transformation occurs
when rhythmic body action is carried out in a
repeated synchronistic postural experience.

Where there is inadequate ego-Self I-
Thou relationship either through denial in
secondary personalization, or ego
identification with the archetype in ego
inflation, the potential healing power of the
Self is not constellated. Clients experience
of loneliness, bodily emptiness,
fragmentation, and a lack of appreciation for
symbolic work emerges with the former and
with the latter an inability to live in the
mundane life and to have a realistic
assessment of physical as well as
psychological limits predominates. The
individual can be seen always moving away
from the body center, extending into reach
space and at times falling because s/he has
gone beyond what is physically possible.

Mythic Themes in Body-Movement Assessment

Uroboric and Post-Natal Embryonic Phases

Much of what belongs in this section has been discussed under the mother complex as well as in the discussion of Mahler's symbiotic phase of development. When this stage is constellated, clients will frequently find themselves submerged in water, gestating in a safe container. Since a fetal neonate cannot talk or conceptualize, the therapists verbalizations are predominantly received for their tonal quality rather than their content. Very little movement should be observed. Warmth and physical comfort is of prime importance. The client should not be expected to maintain a seated position and may need some form of umbilical connection to the therapist. Holding and rocking is, of course, an appropriate consideration given the presence of the mirroring transferential container. Figure 5 is a patient's representation of the constellating self within the symbiotic transferential container. Of note is the fact that her conscious self had never come across a uroboros and that this archetypal batik emerged from her objective psyche.

Second Matriarchal Phase

Themes of birthing frequently manifest themselves in authentic movement experiences when this phase is re-embodied. Here clients may roll themselves up in material or place something heavy on top of themselves. Birthing may take several sessions or develop in a matter of minutes. One individual was seen to climb out of a primordial swamp in which she had been submerged. Another came through a tunnel. Figure 6 is another batik

Figure 5. Uroboros.

Figure 6. The birth of the Self.

from the same woman as figure 5. Here I as
the transferential object am beginning to be
differentiated from the uroboric snake and in
the center I am giving birth to her self
depicted as a flower.

Chthonian Stage

Themes in which the individual is being
chased by monstrous dark figures emerge in
dream material and need to be enacted.
Children and people in so-called "primitive"
cultures understand the importance of the
embodied identification with the aggressor
and its significance becomes clear to the
client in the enactment.

A sense of something dark, omnious,
instinctual from the underground can also
emerge in active imagination movement as the
power of the Great Mother continues to
maintain a strong hold in this final phase of
the matriarch.

Instinctually sexual images and
movements are also present in this phase. One
individual thrashed and stomped the floor as
an embodied centaur awakening phallic energy.
While one woman depicted her as yet
undifferentiated feminine sexuality in a sea
of mermaids. Figure 7 is a wood cut of her
active imagination experience.

Magic Warlike and Magical Creative Phase

The mythic themes for women in this
phase are similar to those of "Beauty and the
Beast" in which Beauty must come to terms
with the sexually instinctual aspect of the
masculine, externalized first in the father,
and then in the projected animus. One woman

Figure 7. The Undifferentiated Feminine.

(Bernstein, 1980a) spends many hours lying on
the floor in active imagination. She is
locked in a temple with a mildewed furry
beast who is to make love to her in an
unconscious state. Gradually he begins
molting, losing his fur, and finally emerges
as her current lover. The same mermaid
patient carved a figure of Pan--half man,
half goat in a spring pastoral setting
(Figure 8). Here her relation to the
masculine was beginning to be differentiated
from the instinctual.

Another woman rolls her body sensually
around the floor but stops short when an
image of her father emerges. Her mother,
filled with generations of powerful dark
mother complexes, had incessantly berated him
to her daughter as a "beast of a man."

Figure 8. The Instinctual Masculine.

For men in the magic warlike phase, themes of being swallowed or drowning in a stormy ocean emerge and frequently get projected on to the female therapist.

Separation from the matriarch was graphically enacted by one man who had brought in a sphinx-like mask. He shared as well a tape of an improvisational piano piece he had composed to the tune of "If I only had a brain" from the Wizard of Oz. For him, however, it was his heart or eros connection to his own anima that he was looking for which had been imprisoned by the Great Mother. While one of the group members placed the sphinx mask on, he, like Oedipus, was asked his riddle. For him it was, "Where is your heart?" "It is with my dead grandmother" was the response. The grandmother, who frequently houses the archetypal protection of the Great Mother, had to be resurrected from the world of the ancestors, ruled over by the darker side of the Goddess. He instructed a woman in the group to lie in a circular section of the room and place the sphinx (now death) mask over her. He moves toward her and yells at the rest of the group to move away. He receives from her in a private interchange and then requests a tunnel-like structure to be built from pillows and mats. With pressure from the other group members, he struggles into the light of the room and a newer, more differentiated relation to his anima.

Solar Warlike and Lunar Cyclic Phases

For men, themes of overcoming their own instincts and fears in an embodied way has sent many an Indian and African pubescent boy into the wilderness to subdue a beast or, through deprivation, commune with the tribal archetypes. One man (Bernstein, 1981, pp. 197-199) describes a sense that he must leave the spot where he is sitting on the studio floor and let go of his boyhood symbolized by a cape. He then eventually moves toward and captures another man (beast) in the dancing group to "bring home to show his father."

For women, the theme emerges of cyclic descent and sacrifice in order to reclaim the repressed feminine and return it to consciousness.

One woman, after initially moving away from her pelvic connection with diagonals into reach space, moves back finally to a grounded centered seated position. As her focus became more introverted, a sense of peace filled the room. "I have to tend my own inner garden--just for me" was her response at the end of the movement experience.

Another woman dreams and experiences a descent into a cave where skulls from her ancestors lay strewn about. It is in this moist dark cold earthy place where she begins to reconnect with her own rich creative source which had been buried for so many years. She is eventually able to see an animus figure who knows the way up out of the cave when it is time.

Heroic and Heronic Quest

Not every client goes on this journey. Many are conscious of the valuing of the reconnection to the Self that a Jungian analytic approach offers, so some self selection process does occur when Jungian movement therapy is chosen.

The hero must find his heroine and visa versa. Psychologically, a woman's animus must be related to and joined with her feminine nature and a man's anima must be united with is masculine aspects.

The man described previously who during a group ritual brought the beast to his father, then becomes conscious of his need to find "his woman." His anima is projected upon one of the women in the group as they dance pelvically moving toward each other and away in a ritual coniunctio.

In another movement ritual, a man and woman each housing each other's projections of animus and anima respectively enact an elaborate marriage. With long cloth trains carried by others they repeatedly encircle

the group symbolizing the Self mandala of
wholeness within their androgenous union.

Another woman dreams prolifically of
herself as the archetypal maid waiting for
her prince in the castle. At first she can
only see him, then communicate to him
nonverbally. Finally, both have heart
operations and are able to begin the needed
relationship.

Her authentic movement experiences then
began to show fuller connection to her
pelvis. Through the use of a guided image of
rays of golden light penetrating her
vaginally, this same woman experiences the
powerful constellation of the paternal
uroboros.

The final phase culminates in the
reconnection with the Self as the guiding
archetype and a shift in the ego from the
external to a more internal less egocentric
relationship to the objective psyche.

Like Christ, Osiris and Dionysus man
needs to descend and risk death and
dismemberment in order for resurrection and
rebirth to occur. With this final
transformation comes the ego's awareness and
subordination to a transpersonal center.

Figures 9-14 are a series of sculptures
created by a male patient spanning his heroic
quest which began in the matriarchate with a
deeply entrenched mother complex, smothering
his relationship to his yet undifferentiated
anima as well as to women in his life. Figure
9 could be likened to many fertility goddess
sculptures when the reign of the Earth
goddess was not yet overthrown by the
patriarchal Judeo-Christian tradition. Her
massive thighs dominate the scuplpture as did

his mother's demands that he remain a puer
caught in the early matriarchal stages of
development.

Figure 9. The Matriarchute.

Figure 10 is entitled Madonna and Child
and was created when the paucity of genuine,
good enough mothering began to emerge in his
material. Here the self a small, white,
marble carving with an empty, concave center
is balanced precariously on the rigid limbs
of the mother.

As I began to feel a wounded, frightened
child self through the somatic
countertransference (discussed in greater
detail in Chapter 6), he too was drawn closer
to the infant within. Sessions were spent in

Figure 1Ø. Madonna and Child.

his bodily awareness of an imprisoned, empty
self (see figure 11), who through dream and
body movement active imagination work he was
able to finally nurture and heal himself.

The next three sculptures bring him into
the heroic quest toward an androgenous
totality. The struggle for the search for the
Holy Grail influenced this sculpture (see
figure 12) of two decapitated knights who
remain suspended in the negative mother's
power while a menacing black cat climbs
overhead. A more positive relationship to the
archetypal mother and the feminine was needed

Figure 11. The Imprisoned Wounded Self.

to enable the anima to emerge. Whitmont (1982) writes of the grail:

"The grail is a wondrous vessel, a wellspring of life-giving, life-restoring waters, and a cornucopia of nourishment, a cup made of Helen's breast. It is in the case of the goddess or a beautiful maiden. It is an endless source of food and sustenance, of joy, pleasure, and feasting as well as of the ecstasies of Venus. In medieval lore, vessel, Grail and womb, as well as lapis ('stone'), were still synonymous images of Mary, the mother of God" (p. 154-155).

Figure 12. Dismemberment and the Grail Quest.

Figure 13, heralded by dreams and active
imagination work depicts the discovered anima
(female marble torso) found at last in the
larger encasement of the mother. The final
sculpture (figure 14) depicts the three
dimensional integration of the feminine with
the masculine. He described the relationship
between the curves (feminine) and lines and
angles (masculine) in the piece which "rises
and fails", cyclically depicting his
progression toward individuation.

Figure 13. The Anima Discovered.

At this time, he was able to commit
himself to a stable, long-term relationship
with a female partner and reflect on his
relationship to his spiritual core.

Edinger (1972) writes, "When a woman (or
the anima in man's psychology) encounters the
Self, it is often expressed as celestial
impregnating power. Danae, while imprisoned
by her father, was impregnated by Zeus
through a golden shower. Similarly, the
annunciation of Mary is commonly depicted
with impregnating rays from heaven" (p. 70).

One woman (Bernstein, 1981) begins an
active imagination movement experience
through a calling to her father. She then
moves in archetypal gathering motions and
finally rests in a receptive centered seated
position. I feel the room fill with a numinous energy. When the experience ends, she

Figure 14. Hieros gamos; Androgeny.

comes over to where I sit and I see a
radiance eminating from her face. She had
felt a shaft of energy enter her vaginally
and shoot up her spine and go out through her
head.

She had been impregnated by the
archetype and came to experience her own
deeply feminine core in relation to the Self.
Figures 15 and 16 are a client's sculpted
examples of giving birth to the Self. In
Figure 15, flowers emerge from a pregnant
woman. In Figure 16, a birthing of the Tao
yin/yang unity of opposites begins to crown.

Figure 15. Pregnant Woman giving birth to Self.

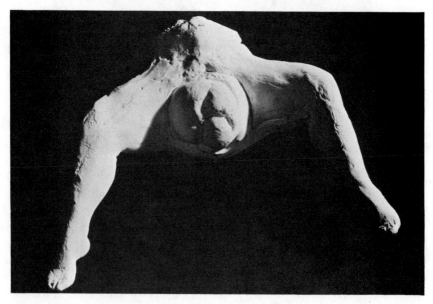

Figure 16. The Crowning of the Yin/Yang Self in the Birth of the Self.

Object Relations in Analytically Oriented Movement Therapy

Archetypal Embodiment

Body movement has a direct effect on the dynamics of the psyche (Whitmont, 1982). Analyst Whitmont (1982) writes, "Enacting rather than acting out our personal complexes enables us to become conscious and cooperative participant spectators rather than unconscious victims of the drama of our lives. Through such consenting action participation, we can become witnesses of the drama of our own tragedia and comedia of the song and dance of the goat god in ourselves, of our own painful and often funny evolution" (pp. 256-7).

Talking about and intellectually analyzing complexes and individual devlopmentally based myths without enactment disembodies the experience and isolates the individual from his/herself. By the same token, unconscious based movement without conscious comprehension can at times limit the transformative nature of the experience.

Providing a therapy container which acknowledges both soulful feminine embodiment as well as the solar spirit of masculine consciousness begins to repair the Cartesian mind-body split upon which psychology and psychoanalysis have long rested their laurels (Whitmont, 1982). Active imagination through authentic movement, somatic symbolic and mythic journeys, dream enactment, and group rites and rituals provides the individual with the means to transform the inner death surrounding a frightened, angry, greedy self into an alive fertile state of pregnancy and Self-birth.

141

Within this container, the transitional space of the therapy temenos can enable the individual to experience the transcendent function of the embodied archetype in the enactment of his/her own mythic ritual process whether it be the expulsion from the uroboric paradise, the slaying of a dragon, or the surrender to the hieros gamos. In this play space, the multiple dual natures of the complexes can be personified, dialogued and transformed.

Alchemy as Therapeutic Process

Each new phase and each new differentiation and assimilation of the various complexes in individuation constellates a bodily reenactment of the alchemical process. Alchemy, the ancient art involving the endeavors of making philosophical gold from baser materials, can also be translated as a symbolic illuminatory process which seeks to transform the prima materia of psychic disunity into the golden salvation of Self-hood.

In the initial Negredo stage, there is darkness, chaos, confusion; nothing is figural. The individual must suffer the unknown. Calcinatio or burning themes can appear. This is followed by solutio in which an emersion in the liquid nature of the unconscious occurs. Body boundaries become plyable and subside. The ego, too, can become "water logged". Images of pools, swamps, floods and title waves, as well as themes of fragmentation and corporal mutilation manifest themselves. Edinger (1978) writes of this stage in the alchemical process: "In its extreme form it is wild, irrational, mad, ecstatic, boundless. It is in the service, not of safety, but of life and rejuvenation.

The weak and immature may be destroyed by its
onslaughts; the healthy will be fertilized
and enlivened like the land by the flooding
of the Nile" (p. 74).

In conunctio, szygy occurs: a union of
opposites in the psychology of the
individual. This process is followed by death
or mortificatio. Here a putrifying or rotting
is often somatically experienced. This decay
along with symbols of excrement become the
fertilizer for the resurrection of the self.
Ablutio, or a cleansing under the water, is
succeeded by an ascent or reincarnation in
which the body is reclaimed. The final phase
entails heating the white albedo until it
glows and becomes the gold of individuation.
This reddening or rubedo is the blood of
reanimation. It occurs with the birth of a
higher integrated Self from the union of
opposites.

The god of alchemy is Mercury, for he
can transform himself to any shape from vomit
and excretia to hermaphrodite and spirit
nature. In his dual nature he is able to heal
the infirm, but he needs always to be
contained in the alchemical vessel which
brews up the individuation.

In guided imagination, one woman enacts
a recurrent theme. She is running from
something that has been chasing her in her
dreams since childhood. Finally exhausted,
she stops to confront it. It is a large dark
cloud. It refuses to engage in a verbal
dialogue with her. She finally enters the
cloud and surrenders to the experience of her
own Negredo.

Another woman comes to her second hour
with a body rash. "What are those (foam
bats)?" she asks. "Do you do primal

143

screaming?" Her emotions had been fired from
the initial session and had burned her skin,
screaming to get out. She reports a dream of
her needing to burn her early childhood
family house. Her calcinatio had begun to
flame through her calm exterior.

Another individual comes in session
after session and dissolves into the deep
blue rug of my studio floor. Her animus
possessed ego had finally given way over the
months of treatment so that a new relation to
her embodied feminine ego could begin to
emerge from the "aqua vita" of the
unconscious.

A man moves back and forth from an
embodiment of his anima to his masculine ego
stance. Then, gradually, a szygy occurs as
his body posture manifests their union.

Still another patient lies on my office
floor. After a while, she describes an
experience of rotting like the dead
vegetation that she mulched into her new
garden. Then she returns to the supine
position for the rest of the hour quietly
honoring this needed somatic mortificatio.

The themes of death long present lift
for another in a group who brings in a
numinous experience in a dream with Christ:
the symbol of the birth, death, resurrection
process of the indiviudating Self. With
others witnessing she dances a dance which
she says has been "pregnant" in her for
months. She titles it "The dance of myself".
The blood of life coursing through each
muscle had reanimated her body and with it,
the birth of a more integrated self.

Therapeutic Process

Schwartz (1982) delineates two stages of the therapeutic process in object related Jungian analysis.

In Stage One, a transformation from the compulsive non-reflective doing of the masculine/animus realm evolves unto a capacity to be. This phenomena is exemplified by a patient who even before sitting would begin to talk incessantly about all the things she had to do and how "stressed out" she was. When I initially suggested she allow herself to be in the room and attend to her bodily cues, she began by cracking her neck and picking her legs up, stretching and extending them to her head as if they were inanimate objects. Only when she was able to tolerate being with herself could she begin the descent into Stage Two. In this final phase, the "phenomenology of the Self" appears. Schwartz (1982) writes,

> "For the Self that now appears has its own autonomous will that threatens to take the person into depths he or she would much rather avoid. These depths and mysteries are associated with the archetypal feminine" (p. 22).

As with the Eleusinian mystery rites of Demeter-Kore, the individual must embody the experience in order to be transformed. Schwartz (1982) continues,

> "This way of Eleusis differs from the narcissistic solutions of idealization and grandiose control. It is a way that sacrifices power and lofty notion of spirit for the sake of its Dionysian embodiment, hence a vision of lesser light. It is a way that values

depression and rage the emotions of the
depressive position--and also terror and
chaos" (p. 150).

This descent into the feminine was
deeply felt by a woman in analytic movement
therapy who descended into the darker realms
of her core self to find and embody a wounded
prickly creature who had retreated into a
corner many years ago lest she be eaten by a
devouring witch. Fear filled the room and her
own body. The fear had no words since it
originated at a preverbal state. Cornered,
the vulnerable self at first slashed out and
needed to reawaken the agonizing yowls and
rage before the pricklies melted into soft
strokable fur.

Therapist as Initiator

It is only those who have been through
the ancient mystery rites which served to
reunite the initiate with the eternal round
of death and rebirth and the Dionysian
wholeness of body and mind that could guide
others in the experience. And so it is with
the analytic movement therapist. The embodied
experience of transformation that comes not
just from a transferential relationship but
also, and most importantly, from a somatic
connection to the transpersonal Self must be
part of the therapist.

"It is a spirit of the body, a spirit in
matter than resurrects, has its own
numinosity" (Schwartz, 1982, p. 144). And it
is that experience of the embodied numinous
that the therapist must know in all its
manifestations. Whether it be embodied death
or rebirth, surrender to agony or the
ecstatic, it is all part of the alchemy of
living.

146

Life is power at play. Shiva or Dionysus dancing" (Whitmont exclaims (1982, p. 245). And in order to help guide others, the therapist must be "dancing."

Case Study: Jungian Object Relations and Self Psychology

When Kate entered my studio-office for the first time, I was aware of my bodily reaction to what felt to be a configuration of sharp angles and even sharper stares. I felt as if the lines of the circular bay where we sat were being penetrated and assaulted. Elbows jabbed the cushions in spoke-like backwards motions as her body repelled itself from their softness. Instead of yielding to the potential comfort and safety of the container, she chose to sit with a bound vertically erect body attitude-- a clear somatic statement that her animus was in charge of her defensive-protective armor and choreography.

Kate's face was a plethora of angles as well. Her bound jaw was held in a gripping relentless smile belying her fear and rage. But what were most figural were her eyes, glaringly devouring every inch of me--ever watchful for the slightest bodily cue of my retreat.

After a sufficient amount of me had been digested, she was able to talk at length about her family of origin, history and reasons for beginning analytic movement therapy.

Family of Origin and Personal History

Kate was 29, the oldest of four children. She was raised under a strict Lutheran doctrine by middle class parents who seemed to be emotionally unavailable. By description, her mother appeared cold and controlling. Anger was not permitted. Like sex, it was sinful. Although Kate was "Daddy's girl," she could not remember a time when he was affectionate with her. Their sole avenue of relationship was through intellectual discourse.

She completed high school and entered college but dropped out after a year to join a spiritual group. Several of the key leaders were clearly inflated with the Christ archetype; and in a rite of "separating the wheat from the chaff," she and her future husband were purged and banished from the core group.

She had been married for seven years to a feeling sensate who served to compensate for her dominant thinking intuitive functions. She had two sons who symbolized her conscious and less differentiated sides of her animus.

Presenting Problem

Kate entered therapy during a marital crisis. She had been having numerous sexual liaisons with puers who she described as being "strong and inspirational but unable to commit themselves." "They are like puppy dogs," she remarked.

When asked whether she felt loved by her husband, she responded affirmatively. Her retort to his caring for her was based on the

148

logic that he must be worthlessly stupid because how could anyone love her.

She realized she was ruining her marriage. She found herself doing "devious things" that ended up being hurtful or destructive to others. Her final and core reason for beginning therapy was that she wanted "to love herself."

Analytic Profile

Ontogeny of Consciousness

Kate was struggling to emerge into the second matriarchal phase characterized by the separation of world parents. With an inadequate facilitating environment for good enough mothering in the postnatal embryonic phase, she had neither a safe holding container nor an attuned pleroma. She therefore was unable to trust the soft buffer of the uroboric mandala of the therapy space. In order not to face the reality of a cold unavailable bad mother, she became the sole bearer of the negative self polarity. Since direct aggression was out of the question with her mother, she only permitted herself indirect maneuvers to release her rage. Frozen in the depressive position, she maintained a two-dimensional vertical attitude and an oral sadistic glare with a taut "toothy" smile. Unit status had clearly not been achieved.

Main Activated Complexes

Mother Complex

Kate's mother comlex was clearly polarized in the negative terrible mother--

the closest constellation to her experience
with her personal mother. In subsequent
dreams and somatic experiences the extent of
the devouring womb image became even more
figural. Maya, the engulfing void, would take
over as her own inner emptiness would attempt
to swallow her up.

Father Complex

What father complex was differentiated
out of the matriarchate was evoked by Kate's
rule-ridden logos father and was thus
unavailable for the vital Eros connection she
needed to value her own feminine worth and
richness. Sex was something to be sneaked
rather than surrendered to.

Animus Complex

With her animus still uncrystalized from
the father complex, she had little or no
access to a psychopomp, anyone who could
guide her toward consciousness.

Instead, her animus served the parental
complexes. When he wasn't engaged in
protecting her through an angular warlike
body atittude inhibiting her shape flow, he
was busy telling her what was right to do to
win others' approval and acceptance. She
would dart off in the saggital plane always
doing for the projected needy self and
negative mother--only to be drawn deeper into
the inner empty somatic void. The remainder
of her animus was projected out on puers who
were only able to relate to her as
instinctual seductress.

Persona Complex

Kate's persona, as well, was tied to looking acceptable in relation to others. She described compulsive clothes buying streaks undertaken so that she would fit "the image." Her mask-like fixed smile provided a friendly extroverted sociable veneer which hid her inner deep depression.

Shadow Complexes

Her shadow figures came out in dreams and active imagination experiences as huge Monsters filled with destructive rage. It was not until much later in the work that feminine figures began to emerge into consciousness.

Ego Complex

Kate's ego was clearly undifferentiated from the mother complex as well. She had externalized much of the Self as a highly judgmental super ego decreeing what was right. Internal shifting toward a more individuated alignment was unavailable. Thus, her undeveloped fragmented ego was an insufficient mediator of her worthless negative sense of self and frustrated rage with a persona which strove toward acceptability.

Self

Only the positive side of the Self was valued as acceptable. "One must strive to be perfect like Christ," was her motto. The darker sides through her negative mother complex and monster rage reactions remain unredeemed and unindividuated.

Archetypal Themes of Transformation

Kate's heroinic identity emerged in an archetypal dream in the first month in therapy in which she was to leave her family and go on an interplanetary journey in a pod (a seed-like spaceship used in the incarnational mythic story of Superman). Significantly, she removes the inappropriate food her mother places in her pod. She lands in a rich meadow and proceeds in an active imagination movement experience into a fertile forest, "The container of the unknown and the mysterious" (Jung, CW13, p. 194). "It's warm and safe. The trees are luminously green. There are no attacking animals. I am tired, I will need to sleep." With that she curled into a fetal position in the circular cushioned space beside me. A clear statement of the need to separate from the negative uroboros of the self-object, and encapsulate her wounded undeveloped self; thus inhibiting the development of the ego-Self axis. She needed to gestate in the safe pleroma of a fertile feminine sphere before she could venture forth in the human realm like superman.

In terms of alchemical individuation symbolism, Kate had been placed in the philosopher's egg (the alchemical vessel) in which she, the prima materia represented in Figure 17 as Mercury, will "cook" and gestate eventually to hatch the gold of Selfhood.

Before two years of analytic work were completed, she would have undergone an alchemical process and descended into the realms and mythic themes of Dionysus and Demeter, and have given birth to herself and begun reclaiming her feminine nature.

Figure 17. Philosophers Egg--The Alchemical
Vessel. From Jung, C.G., CW12.

Transference--Countertransference

In order for Kate to individuate from the second matriarchal stage, a uroboric postnatal embryonic environment would need to be reconstellated with an attuning, good object in a mirroring transference. My body would need to yield to being devoured over and over again and provide the necessary holding and handling, and the circular therapy space would need to be filled with nurturing pleroma allowing for a participation mystique to develop between us.

Analytic Process

Kate related that she initially "tested" me by not bringing in any dreams and by refusing to engage in any active imagination. But she soon relented in the third hour with three dreams. In the first, a giant chases her over the water. She skims across to the other side. When she gets there, she is met by a twin giant who chases her back. As she enacted the giant, she lumbered around the room. "I want to do away with her. I want to do away with everyone." She described him as "purely physical and dumb." This type of giant is typical of the early chthonian phases of development. He is clearly the "quantitative amplification of the ordinary menacing dark side of the bad self" (Winnicott, 1965b). Her eyes tear when I suggset that the giant is her own instinctual anger--long frustrated that would first do away with her rather than harm the potential love object.

In the second dream, her mother-in-law, a more positive nurturing figure, tells her she should take the cantaloupes (her favorite fruit) out of the freezer so they don't get

154

mushed. Dream three has Seth (her sensitive feeling son) falling from a high chair. His legs are caught and become "mush." In these two dreams, her frozen Dionysian connection to her own emotions was to be taken out of the negative cold personal mother. The result in dream three was that the Dionysian cycle with the descent and mutiliation of the symbolic fruit-body had commensed.

In a subsequent session, she brought in and enacted the alchemical journey dream described in the "archetypal themes of transformation." When I reflected back to her that she had begun a journey to Selfhood and that, like an infant, she needed a safe place to begin, she responded by saying that I knew more about her than anyone and that I am like a safety net. She then moved toward me to be embraced.

This safety net proved to be a vital metaphor when in the next session she began an active imagination somatic journey into her inner emptiness. She described a circular spiral bottomless pit in the center of her torso. Six witches surrounded the hole and called to her to dismember herself and throw herself in. As one of the witches, she cackled, raising her arms. "We're cold and empty. We'll bring you down." Alchemically, the witches want her to lose herself in the chaos of the prima materia of the unconscious. Jung (1977, CW, p. 16) writes, "Referring to this state of deadly darkness one alchemist says 'This is a great sign' in the investigation of which not a few have perished" (p. 268).

This spiraling vessel is clearly dangerous. It is bottomless! During this process the soul-Self must not escape. A safe container needs to develop.

155

The dark crones had let me know they were not to be tampered with. For in the next session she reported seducing a stranger in an attempt to fill her painful void. Projecting her negative painful complexes on me, she questioned the realness of my care and positive regard. As she related her encounters, it became clear that sex with these uncommitted puers was a way of feeling in control. Here the shadow dark unassimilated instinctual side of the matriarchate would possess her. She was interested only in mirroring their needs, rarely if ever did she surrender to an orgasm. Straddling these men she would envision herself clawing at them just as the chthonic Dionysian meanads in their orgiastic frenzies would claw and devour animals as they danced through the mountains of Greece.

More rage begins to emerge at the negative transferential object. She reports that I "sound like a judging authority." She started eating large amounts of ice cream to fill the bottomless empty pit with sweet milk. Despite the external storms, however, she continued to maintain an inward focus on her internal void in her authentic movement. At these times she reported feeling closest to herself. She dreamt of needing to find snakes before she can eat. Before she can be nourished by the Good Mother, she will need to relate to these subterranian chthonian reptiles. Jung writes, concerning the alchemical process, "The idea of transformation and renewal by means of the serpent is a well-substantiated archetype" (CW12, p. 144).

Toward the end of the third month, the resistive fragment of her animus came into focus. Kate described it as "stelleto-like" and began to view the extent of its possession of her. Fears of falling to pieces, began to emerge and were tolerated. This process of separatio or divisio elementorium in the first stage of the alchemical process of individuation is frequently translated into an experience of body dismemberment and chaos (Jung, CW16, p. 197). In the fourth month, she was able to stay with her emptiness and consciously elect not to have sex with a potential puer. In an active imagination embodiment she again described a round black empty space, but this time she was able to enter it. She reported, "I am moving around in it. It echoes. On the top right side, there is a tiny light. It is bright, but doesn't shine into the hole. On the left, I can feel the negative energy." This placenta-like kinesphere now had an opening into the light of consciousness. A potential avenue to ascent and rebirth.

The giant now changed to Darth Vader, the dark chthonic father of the unindividuated mother realm in Star Wars. He is still chasing her but this time he makes her his "pet." In her next dream, Darth Vader has a dark women who captures everyone and Kate kills her in order to free herself and others. She was able to associate the dark woman to her mother and began to understand the need to release herself from the bondage to her negative mother complex and the matriarchal phase of feminine ego development.

Again, a wave of rage filled subsequent therapy sessions. She pounded her fists and focused on her mother's inability to give her what she needed and "wrestles [as she described it] with my realness." She dreamt again of the snakes and came to know them as emissaries from the negative mother.

In the fifth month, she had a bodily vision of a cone of energy rising up from her solar plexus into her heart. She had experienced a transformation of the Shakti Kundalini life energy which ascended from the more instinctual realms into the heart Chakra. This alchemical movement Jung (CW 16) describes as "maikipa" the first movement in a process which ends with deification in the devine Self, the Syzgy of Shiva and Shakti" (p. 185). In the session she disclosed being afraid of darkness and of closing the shades at night for fear she would be swallowed up. "My hands are shaking," she related, extending them toward me. I cradled them. She then replied, "I think we should greet each other with a hug when we meet." With the transferential container in full force, she was able to tell her husband that she could commit herself to a monogamous relationship.

Her eyes began to soften and she was able to shape her body into the cushions. In her dreams, Darth Vader now began to relate sexually to her; and Spock, a logos archetypal animus figure in Star Trek, faces her in a bath tub. Both submerge and join in a sexual conunctio. This dream is archetypal and reflects the final process in the first stage of alchemy. In his discussion of the "Psychology of Transference," Jung (CW16) describes this psychic process. This liquid in the bath is Mercurius and "stands for the mysterious psychic substance which nowadays we would call the unconscious psyche" (p. 241). Figure 18 is a woodcut from the alchemical text: Rosarium Philosophorum which Jung utilized in his discussion.

This descent into the unconscious provides the environment for the mystical marriage, the hieros gamos or union of the opposites. The archetype of Logos

158

CONIVNCTIO SIVE
Coitus.

☉ Luna durch meyn vmbgeben/vnd suſſe mynne/
Wirſtu ſchön/ſtarck/vnd gewaltig als ich byn·
☉ Sol/du biſt vber alle liecht zu erkennen/
So bedarffſtu doch mein als der han der hennen.

ARISLEVS IN VISIONE.
Coniunge ergo filium tuum Gabricum dile-
ctiorem tibi in omnibus filijs tuis cum ſua ſorore
Beya

Figure 18. Alchemical Conunctio.

intellectualism, the unfeeling Solar Spock of
Star Trek, is now sufficiently crystalized
from her Oediple father complex to allow for
this conunctio to occur. Although the incest
element still plays an important part (CW16,
p. 304), she had begun to have her own
relationship (eros connection) to her
capacity to discern and discriminate in the
individuating alchemical opus.

In the sixth month, she moved from one
home to another without the help of her
husband who was on a seasonal sales trip.
Emotionally and physically exhausted, she
remained held and cradled in my arms.

In the next session, she reported that she knew the experience of being held by a woman should be familiar, but that it wasn't. She had no memory of her mother nurturing her. The only physical connection she had had was with men. She said she also felt differently about her husband, that she was able to "let him in and feel him." She also realized that valuing him and his love for her had more to do with her own feeling about herself than his worthiness.

Significant dreams followed. She dreamt she is holding a baby and dancing at a square (symbol of wholeness) dance with a young boy. This dream provides further symbolism in her alchemical individuation process. After the mystical union of masculine and feminine aspects of herself, a birth of the self is dreamt. This new hermaphroditic self is frequently depicted in mandalas--the universal of the Self archetype. Here the appearance of the square dance speaks of such a quaternity indicating the possibility of order and wholeness. Then a dream bringing forth the separation of world parents emerged. In the dream a crescent moon shifts back and forth from left to right. Then it forms a whole sphere and radiates light. She felt it meant the destruction of the world. In active imagination, the moon is to engulf the earth and turn everything into pure energy to be transformed into a new creation with sun and moon. The alchemical hermaphrodite (Figure 19) created in 1752 depicts such a psychic phenomenon.

Within the alchemical transferential process, there occurs a descent into the feminine-lunar sphere in which the ego-earth gets devoured in a regressive transference. The positive mother transference that had developed could now allow for a symbiotic

123. Hermaphrodite.—*Hermaphroditisches Sonn- und Mondskind* (1752)

Figure 19. Sun and Moon Alchemical Hermaphrodite.

pleromatic merger to take place. Her logos ego complex naturally experiences this as destruction, and, in a sense, her previous ego complex needed to dissolve in the new object container in order for the ego-Self axis to emerge.

Her mythic journey continues when in a dream she is asked to sacrifice her beloved animus-son for the greater good of the people. Like Abraham and Isaac and Demeter with Persephone, she had to disavow her personal world for the Self.

Toward the eighth month, her connection to her own inner feminine nature began to emerge. She described herself as being "spacey" unlike her usual animus-doing self. I suggested that she reconnect and stay within the experience. She free-associated to when she was in her car and had seen a favorite oak tree. Jung (CW13) described the oak as "the prototype of the Self" and thus a symbol of the source and goal of the individuation process. It represents the philosophical tree as well as symbolizing the opus in alchemy (see Figure 20). Jung (CW13) writes, "As the giver of new birth, the mother is identical with the tree. The arbor philosophica is a favorite symbol for the alchemical process, and when Ripley speaks of a crowned maid (virgo redimitia), we at once recognize the anima mundi, the feminine half of Mercurius" (p. 194). As she stood to embody the tree, she remarked, "The tree is like a woman." I stand as well and mirror her movement. She reflects, "I usually feel like a rod when I stand, but this is different-- more connected." I respond that her animus usually had placed her in an operational position and now she is feeling connected to the earth. Kate acknowledges my comment and continues, "The movement is different, too. My animus usually moves me this way: [She gestures in a forward saggital spoke-like motion] but this movement is like this: [Here her movement changes from one dimensional to three dimensional shaping as she gathers using the archetypically feminine "A" scale of Laban's space harmony (Bartenieff, 1980)]. I respond by saying that the first is linear and the latter is cyclic always returning to her pelvis--the central source of her own feminine power. As we both continue to remain grounded repeating the archetypal gesture, I began sensing the room fill with a numinous energy. I had begun the hour feeling sluggish; I now felt replenished as if I had bathed in the goddess's fountain of rejuvenation. After a while, Kate moved to embrace me and we rocked to celtic harp music. She then moved to see her reflection in my eyes.

In the next session, she brought in a dream of a dark hairy subhuman creature who approaches to relate to her. As the creature,

Figure 20. Arbor Philosophica (1622). From Jung, C.G., CW 12.

"I am part of you. I rage on the outside but I'm soft on the inside." She had begun to relate to her wounded self with a more positive feminine healing energy now available to her.

In another session, she stood during authentic movement and exprienced a swirling base of Mercurial energy surrounding her. Later she was able to re-evoke this force in time of need and felt it had a "smooth calming powerful" effect on her.

The most significant personal dream
came toward her tenth month of work in which
she goes to an island and her mother comes
with a bag filled with what she says is
gourmet food. Kate takes it and looks in it.
It is garbage. In the next dream, she is
holding a snake and squeezing its venom out
to protect her and her family. Her mother's
inability to provide the needed attuned
nurturance and sustanance for the development
of the self became clear. The love her mother
felt was of gourmet quality was like so much
garbage. Now Kate had to syphon the venum
from the negative mother complex in order not
to poison her own subjective (internal) and
objective (external) family.

A heroic animus figure emerges with the
power to transform himself into a skeleton to
evade negative forces. The Spirit Mercurius,
the God of the Alchemical Opus, with his
trickster elusive power had re-entered her
mythic dream world. The following week her
clothing and demeaner were richly feminine.
She had dreamt of a hieros gamos between she
and this animus figure who had transformed
himself into heroic form. It had had a
powerful effect on her.

In an active imagination experience
during the session, she lies down and moves
in a slow sensual manner. She later described
digging in rich dark earth that is "teeming
with life." She related that she used to not
like darkness but now she values its
richness. The negative devouring dark mother
had shifted and a relationship to a positive
Earth Mother had emerged. The prima materia
of the first stage of the alchemical
individuation process had become golden
potential.

After a year she dreamt of giving birth
from a joined uterus of two women--one
mystically spiritual, the other "earthy."
Both aspects of the Goddess Inanna are
reflected here. It is a beautiful girl baby
who smiles at her. A positive self figure had
finally been born in her. In another dream
the same night, she stands in a circle with
different aspects of herself giving money
[originally felt to have been from the
goddess (Luke, 1980)]. An animus figure
wants more. I suggested to her that the
little girl of the first dream talk with him.
Drifting into active imagination she smiled
as her eyes rimmed with tears. "He has no
need of extra money, he is with the little
girl." Her greedy animus, previously in
service to a bottomless devouring mother
complex, could now relate to her emerging
self.

The maw was now described as "having a
soft woolen blanket across it."

In the fourteenth month, she complained
that a burgeoning friendship with a woman was
like a "drop in the bucket." When I commented
that a year ago the "bucket" had no bottom to
catch the drop, she laughed. Soon the bucket
was starting to fill and she experienced
herself giving more to her husband, children
and new friends. She also described an
experience of not being alone--as if someone
were walking around with her during the day--
supporting her, valuing her. She had
experienced object constancy in which the
positive internalized good mother complex
continued the healing and filling from
within.

Post Script

Kate called a year later for a double
hour appointment. She had begun a new

alchemical process and was needing some
assistance in allowing the solutio to emerge.
She described a retensing of her jaw, and in
active imagination expressed a scream which
evolved into an emphatic, "No!". The "no" was
to viewing her life quantitatively; it was
also a refusal to remain the receptical for
her husband's projection of his negative
mother complex and a demand for him to do <u>his</u>
inner work. She was struggling to maintain
her connection to her sense of self and a
relationship to the individuating power of
the Self.

As she attended to her inner sensate
experience, she began hearing the sounds of a
symphony tuning up. I smile at her as she
relates this experience. She retorts, "You
may smile but it is awful to listen to!" I
respond, "It may sound like cacaphony now but
all the inner parts of you need to tune their
psychic instruments of expression in order to
play the symphony of your individuation."

She tears. I ask her what that symphony
might be. She re-enters the imaginal space,
and then responds, "You know, at first I
thought it should be something with great
bravado; but what came out was Handel's water
music."

With the emergence of the needed solutio
that could dissolve her body tension, I
suggested she go home and listen to the
music, allowing it to enter her body, and
guide her into the inner qualitative life
from which she would find the Tao of this
next phase of her individuation. Feeling able
to continue her journey on her own, she
thanked me and departed.

Bibliography

Avstreih, A. "The Emerging Self: Psychoanalytic Concepts of Self Development and Their Implications for Dance Therapy." American Journal of Dance Therapy, 1981, vol. 4, No. 2. 21-32.

Bartenieff, Irmgard. Body Movement: Coping with the Environment. New York: Gordon and Breach Science Pub., 1980.

Bernstein, Penny, and Bernstein, Lawrence. "A Conceptualization of Group Dance Movement Therapy as a Ritual Process," American Dance Therapy Association Monograph III, 1974.

_____. "A Mythologic Quest: Jungian Movement Therapy with the Psychosomatic Client," American Journal of Dance Therapy, Spring, 1980a.

_____ and Carafelli, Enzo. "An Electromyographical Validation of the Effort System of Notation," American Dance Therapy Association Monograph II, 1973a.

_____. "Authentic Movement as Active Imagination." The Compendium of Psychotherapeutic Techniques. Jusuf Hariman, Ed. New York: Charles C. Thomas Pub., 1982.

_____ and Hall, Leah. "Cross-Cultural Puberty Rituals and Jungian Dance Therapy," paper presented at First International Dance Therapy Association Conference, Toronto, 1977.

_____. "Dance-Movement Therapy" <u>Psychotherapy</u> <u>Handbook</u>, Richard Herink, Ed., New York: New American Library, 1980b.

_____. (Ed.) <u>Eight</u> <u>Theoretical</u> <u>Approaches</u> <u>in</u> <u>Dance-Movement</u> <u>Therapy</u> (Third Edition). Dubuque: Kendall/Hunt Publishing Company, 1979.

_____ and Garson, Blaine. "Pilot Study in the Use of Tension Flow System Movement Notation in an Ongoing Study of Infants as Risk for Schizophrenic Disorders," <u>Dance</u> <u>Therapy--Depth</u> <u>and</u> <u>Dimension</u>, Delores Plunk, Ed. ADTA, 1975b.

_____. "Range of Response as Seen Through a Developmental Progression," <u>What</u> <u>is</u> <u>Dance</u> <u>Therapy</u> <u>Really</u>?, Govine and Smallwood, Eds. ADTA, 1973b.

_____. "Tension Flow Rhythms as a Developmental Diagnostic Tool Within the Theory of the Recapitulation of Ontogeny," <u>Dance</u> <u>Therapy--Depth</u> <u>and</u> <u>Dimension</u>, Delores Plunk, Ed. ADTA, 1975a.

_____. and Singer, David, Eds. <u>The</u> <u>Choreography</u> <u>of</u> <u>Object</u> <u>Relations</u>. Keene: Antioch University, 1982.

_____. <u>Theory</u> <u>and</u> <u>Methods</u> <u>in</u> <u>Dance-Movement</u> <u>Therapy</u>. Third Edition. Dubuque: Kendall/Hunt Publishing Company, 1981.

_____. "The Union of the Gestalt Concept of Experiment and Jungian Active Imagination," <u>The</u> <u>Gestalt</u> <u>Journal</u>, Fall, 1980c.

Blanck, Gertrude and Rubin Blanck. Ego
    Psychology II: Psychoanalytic
    Developmental Psychology. New York:
    Columbia University Press, 1979.

Chaklin, Harris. Marian Chace: Her Papers.
    Columbia: ADTA Publications, 1975.

Dewald, Paul A. "Transference Regression and
    Real Experience in the Psychoanalytic
    Process," The Psychoanalytic Quarterly,
    Vol. 45, 1976.

Diagnostic and Statistical Manual of Mental
    Disorders: DSM III. Washington, D.C.:
    American Psychiatric Assoc., 1980.

Edinger, Edward F. Ego and Archetype. New
    York: Penguin Books, 1972.

____. "Psychotherapy and Alchemy. III
    Solutio," Quadrant, Vol. II, No. 2,
    1978.

Erikson, Erik. Childhood and Society. New
    York: W. W. Norton and Co., 1963.

Fairburn, W. Ronald. Psychoanalytic Studies
    of the Personality: The Object Relation
    Theory of Personality. London: Routledge
    and Kegan Paul Ltd., 1976.

Fenichel, Otto. The Psychoanalytic Theory of
    Neurosis. New York: W. W. Norton and
    Co., 1972.

Fordham, Michael. Children as Individuals: An
    Analytical Psychologist's Study of Child
    Development. New York: G. P. Putnam's
    Son, 1970.

Freud, Anna. Normality and Pathology in Childhood. New York: International Universities Press, 1966.

____. The Psychoanalytic Treatment of Children. New York: Schocken Books, 1966.

Freud, Sigmund. An Outline of Psychoanalysis. New York: W. W. Norton and Co., 1949.

Giovacchini, P. Treatment of Primitive Mental States. New York: Jason Aronson, 1979.

Guntrip, Harry. Psychoanalytic Theory, Therapy and the Self. New York: Basic Books, 1971.

Greenson, Ralph. The Techniques and Practice of Psychoanalysis. New York: International Universities Press, 1967.

Hall, Nor. The Moon and the Virgin. New York: Harper & Row Pub., 1980.

Harding, Esther. Woman's Mysteries. New York: G. P. Putnam's Sons, 1971.

Hartman, Heinz. Ego Psychology and the Problems of Adaptation. New York: International Universities Press, 1958.

Jung, C. G. Psychological Types. Vol. 6 CW., Princeton: Princeton University Press, 1977.

____. Psychology and Alchemy. Vol. 12 C.W., Princeton: Princeton University Press, 1977.

____. Symbols of Transformation. Vol. 5 C.W., Princeton: Princeton University Press, 1976.

_____. The Practice of Psychotherapy. Vol. 16, C. W., Princeton: Princeton University Press, 1977.

Kernberg, Otto. Borderline Conditions and Pathological Narcissism. New York: Jason Aronson, Inc., 1979.

Kestenberg, Judith. "Childhood and Adult Pathology," Journal of Hillside Hospital, XVII, April-July, 1968.

_____. Children and Parents. New York: Jason Aronson, Inc., 1975.

_____. "Notes on Parenthood as a Developmental Phase," paper presented at the American Psychoanalytic Association, Denver, 1974.

_____. "Prevention, Infant Therapy, and the Treatment of Adults," International Journal of Psychoanalytic Psychotherapy, Vol. VI, 1977, pp. 339-396.

_____. "Rhythm and Organization in Obsessive-Compulsive Development," The International Journal of Psycho-Analysis, XLVII, 1966a. pp. 151-159.

_____. "The Role of Movement Patterns in Development: I. Rhythms of Movement," Psychoanalytic Quarterly, XXXIV, 1965a, pp. 1-36.

_____. "The Role of Movement Patterns in Development: II.," Psychoanalytic Quarterly, XXXIV, 1965a, pp. 517-562.

_____. "The Role of Movement Patterns in Development: III. The Control of Shape," Psychoanalytic Quarterly, XXXVI, 1967a, pp. 359-409.

171

_____. and Mark Sossin. The Role of Movement Patterns in Development II. New York: Dance Notation Bureau, 1979.

_____ and Weinstein, J. "Transitional Objects and Body-image Formation." In S. Grolnick and L. Barkin (Eds.), Between Reality and Fantasy: Transitional Objects and Phenomena. New York: Jason Aronson, 1978.

_____. "Self-Environment and Objects as Seen Through the Study of Movement Patterns," Unprinted manuscript, 1968.

_____. "Suggestions for Diagnostic and Therapeutic Procedures in Movement Therapy," American Dance Therapy Association Conference Proceedings, October, 1967b.

Kinsler, Phillip and Karen Winter. "Self Relations and Object Relations in the Development of the Self," Keene, N. H.: Antioch/New England, 1981.

Kohut, Heinz. The Analysis of the Self. New York: International Universities Press, 1977.

_____. and Wolf, Ernest. "The Disordes of the Self and Their Treatment: An Outline." International Journal of Psycho-Analysis, Vol. 59, 1978.

Laban, Rudolf, and R. C. Lawrence. Effort. London: MacDonald and Evans, 1947.

_____. The Mastery of Movement. London: MacDonald and Evans, 1960.

Mahler, Margaret. On Human Symbiosis and the
    Vicissitudes of Individuation. New York:
    International Universities Press, 1968.

____, Fred Pine and Anni Bergman. The
    Psychological Birth of the Human Infant:
    Symbiosis and Individuation. New York:
    Basic Books, Inc., 1975.

Maslow, A. H. Motivation and Personality. New
    York: Harper Bros., 1954.

Meissner, W. Internalization in
    Psychoanalysis. New York: International
    Universities Press, 1981.

Neumann, Eric. The Origins and History of
    Consciousness. Princeton: Princeton
    University Press, 1973.

____. "The Psychological Stages of Feminine
    Development." Translated by Rebecca
    Jacobson from Zur Psyhologie des
    Weibliche. New York: Kristine Mann
    Library, undated.

Perera, Sylvia Brinton. Descent to the
    Goddess. Toronto: Inner City Books,
    1981.

Schilder, Paul. The Image and Appearance of
    the Human Body. New York: John Wiley &
    Sons, Inc., 1964.

Schwartz-Salant, Nathan. Narcissism &
    Character Transformation. Toronto: Inner
    City Books, 1982.

____. Notes from Workshop on Borderlines and
    Class on Transference and
    Countertransference, New York: The C. G.
    Jung Institute, 1983-4.

Siegel, Elaine. "Breathing Together."
    Smithtown, N.Y.: Suffolk Child
    Development Center, 1978.

Singer, June. Boundaries of the Soul. New
    York: Doubleday, 1973.

Spitz, Rene. The First Year of Life: A
    Psychoanalytic Study of Normal and
    Deviant Development of Object Relations.
    New York: International Universities
    Press, 1965.

Sullivan, Harry Stack. The Interpersonal
    Theory of Psychiatry. New York: W. W.
    Norton and Co., 1953.

Sutherland, John D. "The British Object
    Relations Theorists: Balint, Winnicott,
    Fairbairn, Guntrip," Journal of the
    American Psychoanalytic Association,
    Vol. 28, No. 4, 1980.

Von Franz, Marie-Louise Puer Aeternus. Santa
    Monica: Sigo Press, 1970.

Whitmont, C. Edward. Return of the Goddess.
    New York: Crossroad, 1982.

Winnicott, D. W. Collected Papers. New York:
    Basic Books, 1958.

_____. Mother and Child. New York: Basic
    Books, Inc., 1957.

_____. Playing and Reality. New York: Penguin
    Books, 1971a.

_____. The Family and Individual Development.
    London: Tavistock Pub., 1965a.

____. The Maturational Processes and the
Facilitating Environment. New York:
International Universities Press, 1965b.

____. Therapeutic Consultation in Child
Psychiatry. New York: Basic Books, Inc.,
1971b.

Chapter 3

Family Therapy in Motion: Observing, Assessing, and Changing the Family Dance

Judith Bell M.F.C.T., ADTR*

Introduction

Our feelings, beliefs, and behaviors develop within tne context of our family of origin and are maintained within the context of our current family. An understanding of family dynamics makes any therapeutic approach more potent. Working with the family unit supports individual growth and individual psychotherapy using a family perspective, stimulates change in the entire family.

The use of movement to observe family interactional patterns, to assess the nature of the family system, and to create positive

---

*Judith Bell is a licensed Marriage, Family, and Child Therapist. She is the past director of the Creative Arts Therapy Graduate Program at Antioch University San Francisco and is currently on their faculty. Ms. Bell also offers private training in her approach and is engaged in private practice with individuals, couples, families and in organizational development.

change can benefit movement therapy students and clinicians working with individuals, groups, or families. Feelings and beliefs about the past, present, and future become alive in the therapy session as movement is used to deepen family members' experience and to catalyze change. By creating a new language for the family dance, spontaneous and unexpected behavior emerges.

My hope is that after reading this chapter, your work, and your personal and family life will become richer and more satisfying as you explore the application of these principles. My experience of myself, my family, and my clinical practice continue to be sources of surprises, change, and growth for me and my family.

As I reflect on my attempt at integrating movement and family therapy, I find that my perceptions of the world, my attitudes about change, my approach to growth, and my belief in movement have their origins in my past. Tracing these ideas from the beginning to the present has been rewarding in penetrating my understanding of my theory and practice. I hope that you, the reader, travel back into your own family of origin to discover the roots of your feelings, beliefs, and approach to movement therapy.

Genesis

The Ocean

I grew up by the ocean where I spent many hours playing in the water and on the beach. Here I first learned about movement;

that movement was the basis, the source of all things; that watching movement was watching the flow of life.

I was struck with the never ending movement of the water. No wave clearly began or ended. A wave would swell and grow and eventually become a roller which broke and cascaded furiously to shore where it spread out in the sand, only to mysteriously begin pulling back into the ocean with a force that pulled me until I almost lost my balance. The wave pulled sand out from under my feet so that I had to use all my strength to remain standing. Then the wave receded and disappeared into the ocean of waves, joining the rolling forces of the next breaker.

I watched this dance of the waves, felt it with every pore of my body as it gently lapped against me, as it crashed into me, rolling me around and spitting me out. All of me experienced the constant motion of the water without beginning and end. All of me experienced constant motion and constant change.

As far as I could see, ocean stretched out in a never ending expanse of water. It had no constraints, no limits, yet was usually contained by the shore. I remember the hurricanes that tore houses off their foundations, leaving a gaping hole where a house and a porch once stood. I feared the ocean, knowing that the force of this flow gone out of bounds could demolish anything.

The ocean provided me with a wide range of experience as I felt the water gently lapping against and encircling my toes, then crashing painfully against my back, toppling me over. One day the ocean was quiet and calm, the next, waves crashed onto the beach, as if trying to reclaim the shore. I felt love and fear, pleasure and pain; the indescribable pleasure of the cold, clear water on my body, the discomfort and pain of being dashed asunder, swallowing what felt like a gallon of salt water.

In the ocean I began to develop movement empathy. I learned about going with the flow and going into the force, into the resistance. If I paid close attention to the movement of the water I was able to stay with the rollers where the ocean swelled and diminished gently. If I were inattentive, the waves pulled me into shore and I found myself face to face with a breaker. If I used my strength and advanced into the breaker, leading with my shoulder and side, the wave crashed over me, leaving me unscathed.

The shifting patterns of the sand also showed me that nothing is static nor permanent. I found that if I did not hold onto something, it changed. A magnificent sand castle, sparkling in the sun could melt into soft hills in an instant of water. I built structures, tore them down, and built anew. These experiences became the basis for my understanding that pain comes from being unhappy with what is, and fear from not knowing if I can cope with what will be.

Something that amazes me to this day is how the sand can accommodate me totally and not lose its integrity. As a child, I loved to lay in the sand and to push my body down so that the sand reached up and merged with my boundaries. When I stood up, a slight ridge remained only to melt away until the surface of the sand hardly showed my visit. I would dig my fingers into the sand which graciously accommodated my probe. It would accept my poking, pushing fingers and make space for me, close up as I withdrew, leaving only ruffled sand to show what had occurred.

I loved to dig for sand crabs, to feel them tickle my hand, then scurry along the sand and burrow in, leaving only a bubble behind in the wet sand that showed life was there. Each time I discovered one of those little creatures, I was suprised and delighted. It was as if the beach were giving me a gift, showing me a treasure, teaching me that if I watched and waited, something unexpected would emerge.

The beach and the ocean were sources of pleasure, accomplishment and learning. Both allowed me to experience what I could do in the world and how I could be. Paradoxically, I found that I could impact my environment and that I was powerless as one tiny part of a great, big universe.

The water, the sand, the sky, the gulls, the people formed a collage, a symphony, a dance from which I learned about complexity and simplicity, subtlety and clarity. The sights, sound, textures, tastes, smells and kinesthetic experiences created a rich tapestry that constantly changed, reflecting all feelings of my experience.

I learned to appreciate the value and beauty of each and every nuance of change. I perceived how each facet is inextricably bound to the whole, that if one aspect changes, the collage, symphony, dance reflects a different mood, and that each mood contributes uniquely to the whole. Each moment inevitably brings a new moment with a new dance. Though the sand, water, and clouds were constantly shifting, the ocean, beach, and sky were always constant. I learned that change and stability are compatible.

In the magnificance and power of nature,
I felt calm, energized, whole, and a part of
the whole. I felt transformed and infused
with feelings of limitlessness, and a belief
that these experiences and feelings are the
substance that give meaning to life.

My Family

My mother tells me that I always danced.
As an infant, I constantly moved. I bounced
with excitement, something I do to this day.
She tells me that I was naturally graceful,
my movements flowed into each other, even
during what was supposed to be the awkward
stages of childhood. I am told that I was
always expressive, always transparent, and
that I had a facility for communicating
through dance. I attribute much of this to
the fact that I was encouraged to express
myself. I do not remember being told to sit
still and act grown up, or to stop jumping up
and down. Demonstration of feelings, artistic
expression, logic, and the derivation of
meaning walked hand in hand in my family.

Everyone in my family loved to move and
express themselves. My grandmother was an
Isadora Duncan-like dancer who had the family
roll like logs on the living room floor and
become characters in spontaneous, improvised
dramas. A grassy field, the beach, or an art
gallery became stages for our family
dance/dramas. A Bohemian type and a member of
"The Graphic Sketch Club" in the twenties, my
grandmother imbued in me a reverence for
beauty, for form, for aesthetics. She taught
me that life is art and that art is a
process.

Memories of these early years of my childhood are filled with dance. A friend's backyard became a dance studio as my mother, my sister, and I bounced and stretched with other mothers and children from the neighborhood. Our dining room table was pushed back to make space for neighborhood dance classes taught by my mother. Gerschwin's "American in Paris" transformed us into bustling city shoppers. Following a performance, whether it had been one of us or professionals on stage, we danced through the streets, alive with joy. I remember my delight as my father watched with pride as I twirled and leaped in the night air.

I remember these family dance experiences with great pleasure for they were times when I felt whole, at one with my family and at one with the universe. They were playful, fun times as well as dramatic and intense. There was a spirit of life, of art, of love, of discovery infusing these times. These are the times I experienced the richness that is possible in family life, what I now call "evolutionary family" experiences.

These memories of my childhood are wonderful but there are those that bring me pain as well. In my family I learned that certain emotions were less acceptable than others. I was not to get angry at my parents for I was told it was disrespectful. In fact, I was not supposed to say "No." My father became unhappy and anxious when I was sad or in pain so I expressed pain for others but not for myself. If I was as dynamic and outspoken as I was wanted to be, my grandmother reprimanded me to "be quiet and give Janis, (my sister) a turn." Externally I became brazen. Internally, I felt ashamed of my self, ashamed of my power. My mother, a dynamic and competent woman, didn't stand up for me against my grandmother, her mother. I didn't know why. In play, I would lock my mother in the closet and not let her out until I felt that she had struggled sufficiently.

I believed that I could take care of my father's pain, help my mother out, support my sister's development, and keep peace in the family if I were only sensitive enough to everyone's needs. My family dance became one of accommodation, mediation, support, and strength.

Dance and Dance Therapy

As I grew up, dancing became a way for me to be all of myself, to let my soul speak. I could express every emotion and attitude and still feel okay about myself. It was the one time in my life when I did not feel as if I had to take care of other people.

I remember the moment in a dance class when, at eight years old, I decided that I did not want to become a professional performing dancer. I knew that I would use dance in some way as I worked with people, that dance would always be an integral part of my life and my work.

When I was fifteen years old, I articulated some of my life dreams: to work with people and their feelings through movement, to work with young children before they were taught how not to listen to themselves, to work with families, using dance as a way to play, to nurture, to fight, and to love each other. I hoped to change the world through dance so that it would be a better place in which to live and to raise children. Knowing of my developing interest, my mother told me of something called "dance therapy" at St. Elizabeth's Hospital. I visited and participated in a dance therapy session with a group of chronic schizophrenics. I then visited Marian Chace at Chestnut Lodge where I observed her work. Both experiences left me thinking, "This isn't dance therapy." The lethargy and lack of emotional intensity did not fit my personal experience and images of dance therapy. I was given a stack of articles which I read voraciously. Some of what Marian Chace wrote touched me; apparently she did understand.

When I encountered the "Wisconsin Dance Idea" (H'Doubler, 1962) at the University of Wisconsin, I felt I had come home. I experienced ecstasy as my professor, Ellen Moore, instructed me to listen to my breathing, to listen to an impulse deep inside me, and to allow my authentic movement to emerge. My body and dance became a source of learning about myself, my interaction with others, and with my physical environment.

In my studies with Moore, I began to trust my authentic dance. I began to learn what I had unlearned as a child, to trust my feelings and perceptions, to realize that my family history and all the members of my family were living inside me. As I danced, images, stories, memories, and feelings from my family of origin emerged. Each time I went to class I learned more about the mysteries hidden inside me. Each time I danced, the story changed.

Moore introduced me to A.A. Leath from the Institute for Creative and Artistic Development. Before meeting him, I read his writing "Essays Celebrating Myself" (Leath,

1967) and I cried. I knew this man could teach me something I wanted to learn about feelings, movement, and living more creatively. I began to study with him in the summer of my freshman year when he moved to Madison. At this time I was exposed to Mary Whitehouse's writing whose words also described my inner experience; and just as with AA's writing, I knew that eventually, I would meet and study with Mary.

My movement process was painful as well as pleasurable. Painful in that I discovered things about myself I did not like, and that my feelings conflicted with my familial beliefs. Leath was instrumental at this point. From him I learned about choice, about self-responsibility, and about priorities; that I could not have my cake and eat it too. I learned compassion. It was all right to take my time. Leath taught me about patience. If I waited and appreciated the moment, change occurred and a decision emerged. I grew to accept myself, to believe that all parts of myself were worthy of being danced. My vision of dance was expanded by A.A.'s definition of a "dance attitude" (Leath, 1967) in which any movement, no matter how pedestrian became dance if the mover assumed an attitude of heightened awareness, discovery, and of the aesthetic.

In short, I was relearning the lessons of the ocean. I continued this process in my studies at The Institute for Creative and Artistic Development in Oakland, California with Eugene and Juanita Sagan. I studied the "Creative Behavior Process", (Sagan, 1965) an approach to learning that stimulates self development and integration, and which fosters "unusual and satisfying" behavior. I became excited rather than fearful about discovering what lurked inside me and eager to let all parts of myself dance.

As I look back, the work I did with Leath and the Sagans was crucial to the development of my work with families. My experience told me that movement held the truth. My desire to understand my family and myself led me on a journey into my family dance.

While still in Wisconsin, I co-led multiple family groups using movement as a vehicle for discovery and enrichment. In each session, we devised movement explorations that focused on particular interactional issues such as setting limits, asking for what you want, and showing affection. Movement became a process for discovery and change.

Later, as I studied family therapy, I realized that I translated family stories into moving images. I became excited by the prospect of integrating movement therapy into family therapy. I had the good fortune to join Michael Geis, M.D. as his cotherapist in family practice at the Family Therapy Center in San Francisco. With him, I integrated movement into structural family therapy. Using recurrent interpersonal issues as a basis for my work, I developed movement explorations for purposes of diagnosis, assessment, and change. Shortly after my affiliation with Michael, Nancy Zenoff and I became professional associates and friends. Also working with families, Nancy and I collaborated in training family therapists to integrate movement into their practice. My association and friendship with both Nancy and Michael contributed greatly to the ideas presented here.

I recently met Will Schutz whose Fundamental Interpersonal Relations Orientation (FIRO) (1958) theory corresponds with what I was experiencing in my work with families. The theory postulates that all human interaction can be understood in terms of three behavioral dimensions: inclusion, control, and openness. Described in greater detail in Theoretical formulations, inclusions refers to association with people, control to influence over people, and openness to transparency between people. Every issue that I encountered in my work with families fit into one of these dimensions. The theory not only reflected my perceptions and practice, it also clarified my understanding of my work and allowed me to go to greater depths in my theoretical formulations.

This paper represents a confluence of theories in dance/movement therapy, family therapy, and group therapy. It forms the theoretical underpinnings of my work with individuals, families, and groups since every person is part of a family and carries a family history. Whether dead or alive, distant or near, family members live in us always. Family therapy is a way to address the whole individual, the individual in a context, and the context. It, too, represents for me a confluence of the past, present, and future.

Theoretical Model

My theory is a synthesis of various theories in the fields of movement therapy, family therapy, and group therapy. I gravitate toward theories that expand my understanding of how I am working and what I am observing. In this section, I address issues regarding movement, the family, and interpersonal dynamics as related to the process of change.

The Moving Individual

Learning Concepts Involves Movement

The experience of motion is fundamental to learning concepts such as me-not me, near-far, comfort-discomfort, satisfaction-hunger, now-then. Sensory data provide the basis for understanding these concepts. All receptive as well as expressive functions involve movement. Hearing involves discerning the motion of sound waves on various parts of the ear. Seeing involves discerning the motion of the refraction of light waves on parts of the eye. Kinesthesis involves discerning skeletal-muscular activity. Thinking also involves movement. The motion of neurons firing create changes in brain waves, heart rate, body temperature, and body chemistry. As these physiological changes occur, a thought is experienced throughout one's entire body. These subtle movement responses, experienced as bodily sensations, form the basis of our memories. Subsequently, a visual image, a sound, or a smell evoke memories that in turn, stimulate movement responses. Recalling a pleasant or an unpleasant experience activates changes in muscular activity simultaneous with the thought. Even with the emergence of abstract thinking, kinesthetic and somatic experience remain the sources of reference for understanding new concepts. It is not an accident that we speak of someone's "grasp" of a subject when we measure their knowledge.

189

Acquiring Beliefs and Feelings Involve Movement

Similarly, what you learn about yourself and others is also apprehended through movement. These perceptions begin in the womb, where you are profoundly affected by your mother's thoughts, feelings, and actions, and by the environment around her. Imagine your fetal experience if your mother is anxious or unhappy, concerned about becoming unshapely and uncomfortable, physically abused or immobilized, cursing your conception, or wishing you were a boy. Imagine how different your experience is if she is happy and calm, proud of her changing body, wanting to make space for you as you grow, active and relaxed, involved in a supportive relationship, and eager for you to join the family. The sensory data from these experiences become the base from which your feelings and beliefs emerge. From birth onward, you continue to gather and store data about your movement experience. These perceptions affect your developing self concept and your understanding of relationships between yourself and others and between yourself and your physical environment. These feelings and beliefs are affected by the movement behavior of those who hold you, care for you, and respond to your desires, explorations, and creations.

Apprehending Truth Involves Movement

Your movement behavior and that of your family members reflect beliefs and feelings which may be out of your conscious awareness. In the context of the family, such subtle movements as widening of the eyes, a sustained sigh, a slight retreating motion

in the chest, or quick tapping of the foot
are pregnant with meaning. These movements
speak truths that you may not have
acknowledged to yourself or to others.

Change Involves Movement

Movement is an obvious medium for
change, since it is the process through which
these perceptions occurred and the reference
for your feelings and beliefs about yourself,
about others, and about the environment.
Feelings and sensory memories spontaneously
and unexpectedly surface when movement is
allowed to emerge and develop in an
exploratory and nonjudgemental process. I
find change begins when creative movement is
used to express a complex of feelings too
difficult to articulate in words, when the
images that lurk in the psyche find shape in
the reality of the physical body. Change
occurs when demons are brought to life and
befriended. As they lose their dictatorial
power, conscious choices about how to live
life replace unconscious driven behavior.

Families

Evolving the "Family Dance" Involves Movement

Just as you were influenced by your
parents and siblings, their feelings and
attitudes about themselves and about you were
affected by you. If you smiled and cooed,
your family had a very different experience
than if you fussed and cried uncomfortably.
Like the waves in the ocean when the
retreating water becomes part of waves
crashing toward the shore, you affected and
were effected by each other. Together you

evolved a family dance, a unique system with its own complex patterns of interaction. As a family, as an organismic whole, you participate in creating and regulating the family dance.

Developing Rules for The Family Dance

The family dance is composed of a continuous multitude of movements that occur simultaneously on many levels. If the number of dancers increases, the number of relationships increases, thereby increasing the complexity of the family dance. Each dancer affects and is effected by every other dancer. Each is an integral part of the whole, so that each dancer's participation influences the dance as a whole.

Together as a family, the dancers create rules that order their family dance, maintaining the level of coherence, efficiency, and satisfaction particular to that unique family. If one dancer changes step, the whole family responds. Depending on the family's feelings and beliefs, it either adapts easily and readily to change, or rigidly and dogmatically attempts to retain familiar patterns.

Though all members of the family are involved in the same collective dance, each member's step is unqiue. Hence, each member has a unique perception of the family dance, and these unique perceptions form the basis for that dancer's feelings and beliefs about the family dance. These feelings and beliefs are attempts to order the chaos of stimuli from the family dance.

Remembering the Family Dance
Involves Movement

The family dance becomes stored in your memory as kinesthetic and somatic sensations, visual images, smells, and sounds. Without your conscious awareness, your sense memory stores information about the kind of behavior allowed in your family, as well as where, when, and within what sequence it may occur. Memories of your family's dance can be activated by a smell, a sound, a touch, a taste, a shift in a movement pattern, a visual stimulus, or a somatic sensation such as your heart swelling with joy. Also, the memories emerge as sensations: olfactory, auditory, tactile, taste, kinesthetic, and somatic. They are accompanied by feelings associated with past events and beliefs about the origins and meanings of those family events.

When sensory memories about your family experience are activated and you become flooded with sensations, feelings, and thoughts, you may recall shifts in movement interactions that you were not aware of before. In a state of heightened awareness, profound meaning is assigned to whether a family member retreats or advances when he or she is approached, whether someone walks faster or slows down when another family member loiters, and whether the family's tension increases or decreases when someone spontaneously expresses a feeling.

Changing the Family Dance Involves Movement

Just as movement is the process through which these feelings and beliefs were apprehended, the family is the context in which they were learned. If the family dance

changes, then feelings, beliefs, and
behaviors change. Unlocking family patterns
is the key to freedom. Without choice,
families remain locked for generations in
family patterns that possess them like ghosts
in a haunted house.

Movement Therapy

Aware of the complex information
communicated nonverbally in families, several
leaders in the field of family therapy are
also aware of the potency of movement as a
technique to catalyze change. Satir (1964,
1972), Minuchin (1974, 1981), Duhl and Duhl
(1973, 1983), and Papp (1973; 1976) stress
nonverbal modalities and have developed
techniques such as family reconstruction;
scene enactments, sculpting, and
choreography.

The integration of movement therapy into
family therapy adds breadth and depth to an
already richly creative field. As I have
integrated movement therapy techniques into
family therapy, I have found a variety of
perspectives to be useful, including
pedestrian movement out of awareness,
creative movement in conscious awareness, and
authentic movement with heightened awareness.
All three may be used for mobilizing and
deepening feelings as well as for stimulating
new behavior. The range of movement
possibilities to which I attend encompasses
large locomotor movement, gestural and
postural movements, and subtle shifts in
breathing, skin tones, and eye contact.

Characteristics of the group's
expression as well as individual expression
are observed and utilized. Since the family
dance is the totality of all the subtleties

and complexities of the movement behavior of the family, all these aspects affect my perceptions of the family and all are the subject of my exploration.

By reaching under the words, into the affect, the subtleties of the family dance emerge. The movement process becomes a journey, a search to find expression for the conflicts, pains, and hopes of the family. The unexpected occurs as feelings, attitudes, and movement become articulated as one. New movements emerge as memories of the past join fears and hopes of the future in an expanded awareness of the present. A subtle shift opens the door to new steps in the family dance. Without being planned, change occurs.

Families in Therapy

Family therapy is a process of transformation. It is about letting the ghosts out of the closets and allowing them to live. It is realizing that love means accepting the dark with the light. In family therapy, you begin to see your parents for who they are, without having to change them. Your mate becomes your spouse rather than a missed parent; your siblings become your friends; you begin to learn from and become ready to parent your children. Paradoxically, as you delight in being a member of your family, you realize that you are alone. Without your parents, your mate, your children, you find that you are alone and that you are all-one. As perceptions change, you become able to let go of unsatisfying patterns of interacting and discover behaviors that are innovative and satisfying. You begin to appreciate the uniqueness of your family dance and to foster its development. As you and your family abandon the fear that you cannot cope with what change might bring, you begin to embrace the idea that the family dance can be an evolution.

When families come to therapy, they are in pain. In most cases, they seek help when all else has failed. Typically, one family member manifest's the family's pain as a psychiatric, behavioral, or physical symptom. Such a family comes to therapy hoping to change the person who they believe to be at the root of their problems, (the "identified patient"). In these families, the expressed goal of therapy is the removal of their symptoms. Some families have the additional goal of achieving personal growth and greater satisfaction in their lives. My work with families tends in the latter direction. I view family behavior as a continuum, with dysfunctional behavior at one end and positive, evolutionary behavior at the other end. My interest is in helping families move toward the evolutionary end of the continuum rather than in simply seeking to remove symptoms.

The Evolutionary Family

There is no such thing as a perfect family. Yet, some families do have more satisfying journeys than others. The behavior of these families tends toward the evolutionary end of the continuum, so I call them evolutionary families. The rules governing this family have the well-being of each family member and the family as a whole in mind, and excitement about personal growth is pervasive.

The movement of this family is innovative and expansive and has an organic quality about it. There is flexibility, surprise, and excitement. Taking risks is a daily occurrance as curiousity and confidence guide each person. Sustainment and quickness, lightness and strength, opening and closing, and all the opposites of which we are capable are found in this family. There is an order that expands and contracts as a living organism, that defies linear thought.

This family uses the wisdom of its past to make sense of its present and to look forward to its future. It focuses its attention on attempts to explore and investigate the environment with curiousity and thoroughness. Such a family confronts situations with acceptance of what is and decides its commitments wisely, by anticipating actions over time. As a result, this family communicates easily and readily, presents itself with pride, and operates effectively.

The evolutionary family has a quality of aliveness, buoyancy and dynamism. It is spontaneously adaptable to change, so that it always has the experience of "fit." It identifies and behaves as a team, with the sense that "we're all in this together." On top of all this, a quality of exuberance and pleasant expectation pervades interactions in this family. In short, this family has all the tools to function in a creatively satisfying manner. Unfortunately, few families can claim this title, though some families have evolutionary behavior in certain areas of interpersonal functioning.

The Dysfunctional Family

Even more distressing is the abundance of the opposite extreme, the dysfunctional

<u>family</u>. The vast majority of families tend
toward the dysfunctional end of the continuum
in most aspects of their behavior. They are
fraught with unsatisfying and counter-
productive behavior. There is no room for
experimentation and discovery. Fear of change
governs this family and rigid rules dictate
its behavior. Pain is pervasive. Love has
trouble coming in because family members are
so busy protecting what they might lose that
they cannot experience what they share. It is
no wonder that family therapy is such a
widely growing field.

The movement in this family is
repetitive and often gets jammed up and
stuck. Its rhythm is either monotonous or
erratic. The family dance has many opposites,
but not much of anything between. The
family's order is either rigid and arbitrary
or lax and chaotic. The family identifies and
behaves as an undifferentiated mass or a
loose collection of disparate parts. This
family feels inordinant amounts of
disappointment or nostalgia about the past,
fear of the future, and pain in the present.
The quality of attention in this family is
either narrow and restrictively singular or
so broad that it becomes diffuse. The
communication in this family is disjointed
and awkward. A dysfunctional family such as
this confronts situations without considering
the context. It has trouble accommodating to
its environment, often denying of what
exists. Members of such a family either make
commitments arbitrarily and foolishly without
accurately assessing a situation over time or
they avoid commitments altogether. Their
presentation of themselves is both pathetic
and courageous as they overcompensate with
bravado or withdraw with self-effacing shame.
It is not surprising that they have trouble

communicating or operating efficiently or effectively.

Interactions among family members have a quality of deadness, restriction, and grimness. They tend to look hopeless, helpless, and lonely. There is little evidence of pleasure, joy, excitement, or eagerness. The family seems out of step and "out of joint" as they fearfully cling to the past and retreat from the future.

Theoretical Formulations

Interpersonal Dimensions of the Family Dance

In my early work with families, I found that certain themes consistently arose. Pain and conflicts relating to issues of contact, of whom related to whom, were frequent. Problems about control, about family leadership and decision making, were equally prevalent. Conflicts about honesty and vulnerability often arose as family members exposed their feelings about themselves and each other.

These recurrent conflicts became the focus of my movement explorations in what I call core processes (Bell, 1979). I define a core process as a constellation of conflictual interactions that revolve around the family's most salient issues. These themes include: boundaries between people and subsystems, inclusion/exclusion, cooperation/ competition, decision making, control, assertion, exchange of affection, giving/ receiving, and similarities/ differences in family members feelings, attitudes, and movement styles.

Because of my predilection toward conceptualizing family interaction in terms of interpersonal issues, I have found Schutz's Fundamental Interpersonal Relationship Orientation (FIRO) theory, (Schutz 1958) to be an efficacious device for understanding both the family dance and the dance between the family and the therapist. Derived from an extensive review of research and theoretical analysis of group behavior, Schutz's theory explains all interactional phenomena through three interpersonal dimensions, inclusion, control, and openness*.

Inclusion

Inclusion behavior refers to associations between people. It has to do with how much contact is desired or sought. Issues of inclusion encompass desires for belonging and togetherness, recognition of uniqueness, commitment to a relationship, and desires for attention and prominence. Underlying these concerns is the issue of personal importance, which is often reflected in fears of being insignificant, worthless, and ignored. "Inclusion has to do with In or Out" (Schutz, 1983).

Control

Control issues have to do with the desire to exert or relinquish authority.

---

*Openness was called "affection" until the first publication of The Human Element in 1980 when schutz changed it to parallel the other two dimensions which are behaviors rather than feelings.

Independence and rebellion describe one end of the continuum, while compliance and submission describe the other. Central to the control dimension are confrontations over role negotiation, power, responsibility, and influence. Underlying behavior in this dimension are feelings regarding competence and the fear of being humiliated. Schutz describes control as having to do with "Top or Bottom" (1983).

Openness

Openness behavior refers to the amount of transparency or privacy sought by people. It has to do with the desire for personal and intimate or impersonal and distant relations. Vulnerability is central in this dimension. Underlying behavior in the area of openness are feelings regarding lovability and the fear of being rejected. Openness has to do with Open or Closed (Schutz, 1983).

Schutz (1958, 1979) postulates that any group of two or more people follow the same developmental sequence in addressing these areas of interpersonal behavior. First inclusion issues predominate, then control issues, and finally openness issues. The sequence might cycle through the group several times, with group members reworking the respective issues until they become resolved sufficiently to allow the group to continue. One dimension is always paramount at a given point in the group's development, though all three dimensions are present at all times. For certain individuals, a particular issue may be so conflictual that it transcends the current group issue. The area of prime concern for a particular member at a given time is determined by the interaction between that person's special

areas of conflict and the currently dominant
group issue.

As groups prepare for termination, they
cycle through the same phases in the opposite
order, first airing feelings about openness,
then control, and lastly inclusion. Group
members' response to impending separation
revolve around the area that is most
conflictual for them (Schutz, 1979).

The Family FIRO Model in Motion

Though families are different from the
ad hoc groups that Schutz studied, I have
found the FIRO dimensions and theory useful
in understanding issues faced by the family
itself and by the group composed of the
therapist and the family. In this section,
family issues that fit into areas of
inclusion, control, and openness are
described. Dysfunctional family behavior in
each area is compared with evolutionary
family behavior. Included in this discussion
are movement parameters that I find to be
useful for observing various aspects of each
dimension.

Inclusion

Inclusion issues have to do with how far
family members are in or out of the family as
a unit and its various component
relationships (Doherty and Colangelo, 1982).
Inclusion conflicts center on defining the
personal and collective space known as
kinespheres. This area of concern is
manifested in questions of belonging and
individual identity, membership in
subsystems, commitment and loyalty, and
personal boundaries and contact.

For the movement therapist, individual
and group attitudes toward inclusion issues
are most readily seen in lateral motility,
(movement through space in the horizontal
plane), in proxemics, (aspects of spatial
organization), and in the shaping of the body
and space in the horizontal dimension.
Relevant to the observation of inclusion
issues are aspects of synchronous,
accommodating, blocking, and bonding
behaviors (Dulicai, 1977), as well as the
quality of attention or focus between family
members.

Belonging and Individual Identity

The members of evolutionary families
feel secure in belonging to the group, yet
free to be separate individuals. The sense of
belonging and the knowledge that the family
as a whole is committed to each individual's
growth reinforce each other. The family's and
each individual's kinesphere is elastic,
expanding and contracting as desired. A high
level of interactional synchrony creates the
sense that partners are well matched, whether
they are dancing together or apart from each
other.

The members of dysfunctional families,
on the other hand, do not feel a balance
between belonging, being a part of the whole,
and being a separate individual. Such people
my feel bound together in a "consensus-
sensitive" paradigm (Reiss, 1981) or they may
feel divided by the belief that it's "each
man for himself" (Ford, 1974). The members of
these families feel either an "emotional
'stuck-togetherness' " in an
"undifferentiated family ego mass" (Bowen,
1978) or a sense of isolation and distance
within a disconnected, individualistic

style of interaction (Hoffman, 1981). For the dysfunctional family, it would be foreign to think of the family as contributing to individuality and visa-versa. The family's and individuals' kinespheres are either rigidly formed or formless. A propensity toward asynchronous interaction makes these families generally look and feel 'out of sync." However, particular pairs may be locked in an eerie dance of synchrony.

Membership in Subsystems. For the evolutionary family, determining which family members are included or excluded from particular subsystems has to do with obtaining optimal satisfaction for each family member and for the family as a whole. (For example, a child may join the parental subsystem temporarily by taking on executive power vis-a-vis other siblings, when that behavior is beneficial for all those involved.) Consequently, family groupings, vary frequently. Accommodating behavior is the rule, and blocking behavior is used for purposes of maintaining physical or emotional well being.

In the dysfunctional family, membership in particular subsystems is either rigid or unclear. Parental children who take on executive power over siblings feel excluded by the parental subsystem because they are not adults and by the sibling subsystem because they are not being treated like children (Colangelo and Doherty, 1982). Pathological triads are created by inclusion and exclusion in these subsystems, which are based on people's fears and desires. Family groupings are invariant, with the same people initiating or terminating contact. Blocking behavior is considerable, as it is a means of excluding people.

Commitment and Loyalty. Evolutionary family members feel nourished and supported by a balance achieved between commitments to the family unit and commitments to career, extended family, friends, and other interests. There is a consensus about issues having to do with the timing of events, their duration, and the quality of attention family members give to each other and to their various commitments.

In the dysfunctional family, questions of priority and loyalty are paramount. Affairs with a person, or the equivalent absorption with a career or an interest are frequent. Issues of commitment are stressed during all stages of the family's life cycle. Priorities are established arbitrarily and adhered to either rigidly or too loosely. There are frequent arguments over who did what when, for how long, and in what way.

Personal Boundaries. In the evolutionary family, involvement in each other's lives feels mutually satisfying for all family members. Everyone freely seeks contact or privacy, knowing that others will do likewise without feeling intruded upon or ignored. Personal boundaries expand and contract in a constantly fluid manner, as all family members use a wide range of near, reach, and far space in relation to each other and with respect for each other.

In the dysfunctional family, everyone feels either intruded upon or ignored. They are either enmeshed in each other's lives to the point of overinvolvement or they are disengaged to the point of little or no contact. Individuals feel either suffocated and craving for privacy or alone and starved for interaction. Behavior tends to be dictated by the fear of engulfment or separateness or by the desire for merger or autonomy.

Attention. In the evolutionary family, each person receives a kind of attention that engenders feelings of significance. Each individual feels equally significant and important in the life of this family, and each member feels free to ask for, receive, and give both narrowly focused and diffuse attention.

The quantity and quality of attention offered in the dysfunctional family leaves each person feeling insignificant and ultimately unimportant. Family members either scrutinize each other using an excess of narrowly focused attention or ignore each other diffusing their attention to the point of being "spaced out". In overattending or in underattending, family members move cautiously or recklessly vis-a-vis each other; no one trusting others to have his or her well being in mind.

In short, in the evolutionary family, issues of membership, commitment, and personal boundaries are handled in such a way as to engender feelings of significance and trust in oneself, in each family member, and in the family as a whole. In the dysfunctional family, the feelings engendered are insignificance, distrust, and fears of being ignored.

Control

Control issues have to do with how family member regulate each other's behavior. These issues are manifested overtly or covertly in conflicts over responsibility, discipline, power, decision making, and role negotiation. Control issues are most readily seen in the way family members seek to influence others. Overt or covert attempts to lead or follow others may be seen in how individuals vary their movement dynamics vis-a-vis each other. For example, one family member deters conflict by spacing out and getting distracted while another avoids conflict by becoming obsessively focused on an inconsequential point. A person rises in leadership, descends in submission, and alternates between the two in ambivalence (Kestenberg, 1977). Within an interactional context, each aspect of movement may be used to influence others' behavior. Family members also attempt to regulate interaction using transactions by changing their proximity to one another, by monitoring the quality and duration of their eye contact, and by assigning punctuation to the order of events. The amount of spontaneity and fluidity in the family's movement yields information about the wielding of power, the level of trust, and the finality of decisions in the family.

Responsibility. In the evolutionary family, each family member carries a share of responsibility, so that nobody feels burdened or inconsequential. In fact, each person is proud of his or her impact on the family system and feels eager to learn and grow by taking responsibility. When assuming responsibility for a feeling, a thought, or an action, people remain balanced around their central axis, with a dynamic attitude toward gravity in what is commonly referred to as being "centered and grounded."

In the dysfunctional family, responsibility means either superiority or culpability. Some family members shirk responsibility by acting innocent or by blaming others or external circumstances, while others shoulder responsibility that is not theirs and assume a holier-than-thou attitude. In such a family, people either feel burdened and resentful or inconsequential and impotent. Responsibility for family problems may be placed on an "identified patient" who manifests psychiatric disturbances, physical symptoms, or behavioral problems. In this family, one member shrinks and retreats in fear while another grows with anger and disapproval. Family members do not appear balanced when assuming responsibility. They look as if they would like to disappear or as if they could sink a ship.

Power, Discipline and Leadership. Power is wielded benevolently in the evolutionary family. Because each person's presence and intentions are respected, an easygoing and optimistic feeling prevails. It is observable in the spontaneous and flowing expression of each person's movement, and in their elegantly lengthening bodies. People in this family align themselves with each other in open affiliations, showing a preponderance of accommodating and syncronous behavior that supports the collective venture.

Discipline is used to facilitate learning and support each person's well being. There is a nurturing quality to discipline in an evolutionary family. This may be observed in the even manner of flow with which people express their feelings and in the gentle but firm way a parent teaches a child through a disciplinary experience. Family members are aware of the impact they have on others and vary their use of pressure accordingly. They take turns leading and following each other depending on the task at hand. As a result, tremendous variety is seen in who approaches or separates from whom.

Shared eye contact reflects the care that is taken to insure that each person feels proud of his or her ability to do each. The evolutionary family has the feeling and look of a balanced seesaw, in that people relate to each other with parity rather than dominance.

In the dysfunctional family, power is wielded arbitrarily and inconsistently, without respect for other family members' intentions. Information about the amount of restriction, the control of anger, and the level of caution in a family may be gathered by noticing the relationship between the level of inhibition in the flow of movement and the degree of expansiveness in the shape of the movement. Two people from different subsystems often join together against or to the exclusion of a third party in an attempt to exert or undermine authority (Haley, 1977). Such coalitions become obvious if one observes redundancies in the proxemics, synchrony, blocking, and accommodating behavior of family subgroups.

Leadership is either rigidly authoritarian (established overtly, or covertly through coalitions), or it is insufficient. Moreover, it is exerted within a competitive struggle for dominance. People continually try to appear one-up or one-down on others in an attempt to exert leverage in the family system. Some indicators of dominance and submission are: who approaches or separates from whom; how people rise and descend in relation to each other; and whether there is a propensity toward prolonged, narrowly focused attention or the aversion of eye contact.

Discipline is either rigid, inconsistent, or nonexistent. It is administered irrationally, inappropriately, and without respect for the individual. It is an attempt to order chaos or gain respect. In this family, discipline and punishment are synonomous, and people feel either overly constrained or "underorganized" (Hoffmann, 1981). People in this family are not aware of their impact on each other, and this insensitivity is readily seen in the prevalent use of high intensities of force vis-a-vis another, regardless of the context. Severe contraint is seen in how people bind their movement and inhibit their spontaneity. Inconsistent or unpredictable attempts to exert control are visible in erratic fluctuations in people's rhythm.

Conflict Resolution and Decison Making. In the evolutionary family, conflicts are resolved openly and are regarded as opportunities to learn. There is compatibility in the ways in which family members gather information, formulate and commit themselves to a solution. Differences are acknowledged and accepted, even invited. People adjust aspects of their movement behavior (space/focus, weight/pressure, time/pacing, tension flow, and shaping behavior) (Laban, 1960 and Lamb, 1965) in order to accommodate to individual differences. Family members are encouraged to play an open part in decision making, which is fair and supportive of each member's growth.

Fighting is clean and to the point. The source of the conflict is addressed, rather than the symptom, so feelings are acknowledged. How family members enter into and withdraw from one another's kinespheres is decided by mutual agreement.

In the dysfunctional family, conflicts are resolved poorly, if at all. False agreement ("pseudomutuality") and false disagreement ("Pseudohostility") keep conflicts submerged and undefined (Wynn, 1963). "Detouring" is used to manage conflict, by either scapegoating or overprotecting a particular family member (Minuchin, 1974). Physical, psychiatric, or behavioral symptoms may further mask and detour conflict. These symptoms emerge when complementary (one-up/one-down) relationships become too skewed and reach what is perceived by the family as a critical point. With conflict, symmetrical relationships often escalate to the point of physical violence or divorce (Hoffman, 1981).

Decision making is as arduous a task as conflict resolution in the dysfunctional family. A high degree of asynchrony and, hence, incompatibility, is seen between individual styles of gathering information, formulating decisions, and making committments to solutions. Individual family members' needs are not taken into consideration, and this neglect is visible in each member's lack of adjustment to the others. In "under-organized" families, decisions are avoided until circumstances create urgent conditions. In fact, making a decision is paramount to being disloyal in these families. Decisons regarding entry into and withdrawal from each other's personal space is done without regard for the other.

People do not take credit openly for their impact on the family system. Hidden loyalties that prevail make every decision a contest, and double-binds are often set up to discourage one or more family members from communicating their feelings about an issue. In the classic double-bind, contradictory

211

messages are sent and any response is penalized (Watzlawick et al. 1967).

Role Negotiation. Evolutionary family members share tasks in a way that supports each person's growth and allows each person to make an important contribution to the family. Nobody feels limited by a self-prescribed or externally assigned role; rather, people feel motivated to achieve their potentials and test the limits of their capabilities. This is visible in the fluidly changing movement patterns as family members relate to one another. Roles are redefined as family circumstances change through the family life cycle. If one person enjoys one thing and someone else another, the two agree, as equals, to be complementary partners; neither feels one-up or one-down. In the evolutionary family, attention is paid to the impact that redefinition of roles has on the relationships between approaching and separating, leading and following, rising and descending, and variations in restricting or freeing movement among family members.

During collective activity in the dysfunctional family, people either look as if they are participating under duress or out of boredom. Family members either work side by side with little awareness of each other's presence, or they work alone in isolation, without any coordination of tasks.

Roles in this family are defined either rigidly or nebulously and serve to establish superiority or inferiority or to alleviate family pain. The effect of role redefinition on relationships among family members is not considered. Fluctuations in the family's movement behavior are either minimal or drastic, creating an atmosphere of deadness or erratic volitility. In any case, redefining roles is difficult, if not impossible, even in the face of circumstances that demand change.

Intention. In the evolutionary family, each family member feels competent. Their bodies exude confidence in their easy going manner, in their erect yet flexible body attitudes, and in their expansive movement. They feel free to experiment and explore new endeavors and new approaches, for in this family there is no shame in making a mistake. No one suffers from the fear of humiliation because everyone's intentions are applauded and supported. Family members' enjoyment of taking risks is seen in the way they move forward with ease and anticipation.

In the evolutionary family, control issues of responsibility, discipline, power, decision making, conflict resolution, and role negotiation are resolved in such a way as to engender feelings of competence and pride in all family members.

In the dysfunctional family, no one feels competent. Family members in such a family often feel impotent and despairing. These feelings are apparent in their passive orientation toward gravity. Their bodies shrink and contract as they retreat into themselves. They move as if they suddenly became exhausted or as if they were steadily losing steam. This family also breeds people who become resentful and resolute in their desire to make a difference, a desire that shows in a desparate struggle against gravity.

No matter what anyone attempts to do, someone tries to pull the rug out from under him or her. Everyone feels afraid of ridicule and humiliation, so experimentation with new

213

behavior is usually too dangerous.
Individuals' intentions are regularly
sabotaged or are implemented with resentment
or pseudoagreement. Family members are either
prepared for flight or they are ready for
attack. Whichever the case, they do not feel
secure in their judgement or their ability to
lead or follow. Any decision made or action
taken is never good enough.

Openness

Openness issues have to do with sharing
private thoughts, feelings, and desires that
pertain to vulnerable parts of the self.
Attitudes toward openness are most readily
seen in how open or closed family members are
with each other. Openness-related conflicts
revolve around feelings of being
misunderstood and unappreciated. The level of
openness in a family may be seen in the
relationship of blocking, accommodating, and
synchronous behavior to the expression of
feelings, thoughts, and behaviors; the degree
of congruence between movement and verbal
expression; the degree of spontaneity, and
the quality of touch and attention used
between family members.

Intimacy and Uniqueness. In the
evolutionary family, intimacy is a way of
life. Every dyad in the family experiences a
relationship that is special and unique to
that pair. This is a family of friends as
well as of parents and children. Rather than
treating each other as objects, the spouses,
the parents and the children, and the
siblings interact in I-Thou relationships.
The family holds the belief that each human
being is special and deserves to be treated
with respect, compassion, and love. In such a

family, each person's self-expression is at least acknowledged, if not accommodated.

People are appreciated for their unique qualities. Total expression of self is supported, and this support promotes the turning of thought into action. A high level of spontaneity may be seen in the easy transitions and the range and versatility of family members' movement expression. Physical contact in this family is nurturing, natural, and spontaneous, as it reflects the affection felt among family members.

In the dysfunctional family, intimacy is feared and avoided. Family members maintain a safe emotional distance in an attempt to protect themselves from possible humiliation, hurt, or rejection. There are frequent displays of "pseudo-affection", or "pseudo-openness," in which family members pretend to be emotionally closer than they really are. People are treated as objects in the dysfunctional family, and feelings, thoughts, and actions are not respected. Family members' attempts to communicate are frequently blocked or ignored. Family members do not have the feeling that they are special or lovable. The small amount of eye contact shared between family members has the quality of either looking past the other person or shooting daggers.

In the dysfunctional family, everyone tries to be the same as everyone else or as different as possible. People are not appreciated for what is uniquely theirs, but rather for how well they play the family game. There are inordinately high levels of both interactional synchrony and asynchrony in such families.

Rules about the display of affection get confused with taboos about sex, and this confusion impedes the natural flow of affection between husbands and wives, fathers and daughters, mothers and daughters, mothers and sons, and fathers and sons. Sexual problems between spouses, promiscuity, and incest frequently occur in these families (Satir, 1972). Touch is seductive, harsh, or nonexistent in these troubled families.

Communication. Communication in the evolutionary family is open and fluid, since each person is truly interested in and enriched by what the other has to offer. This makes for a high level of congruence between family members' verbal and nonverbal behavior. Because people in such families vary the quality of attention they bring to various situations, the feelings underneath people's words are heard and acknowledged, actions find genuine responses, and choices about behavior are based equally on self-satisfaction and the common good. Anything and everything is talked about openly in the evolutionary family. Nothing is considered unimportant if it is meaningful to any family member. This family understands that "you cannot not communicate" (Watzlawick, Beavin, & Jackson, 1967). As a result, verbal content, voice quality, and movement behavior are considered equally important aspects of communication.

In the dysfunctional family, communication is used to regulate emotional distance, and emotional distance regulates communication. Hence family members do not really want to communicate; it is too threatening. Attempts to keep feelings, thoughts, and behavior private reflect the desire to minimize family differences and individual vulnerability to criticism. For this reason spontaneous behavior is nonexistent in the dysfunctional family.

In such a family, any disagreement is experienced as an invalidation of the self or a narcissistic wound that demands retaliation. Family members retaliate by one-upping each other (confirmation of self) or putting each other down (disconfirmation of other). They also find ways to deny that the disagreement has taken place (denial), or that either one of them even exists (disqualification of self or other) (Haley, 1963). The high level of incongruence between verbal and nonverbal behavior in this family reflects family members' feelings of ambivalence about communicating their feelings and thoughts. This manifests in multilevel communication that is rife with denials, ambiguities, and covert messages about which no one is allowed to comment. (The lack of response, however, is itself a response as "you cannot not communicate.")

Truth and Vulnerability. In evolutionary families, honesty and self-disclosure form the basis of relationships. Family members feel free to search their depths to find their truth and to become transparent as there is no fear of rejection in this family. Seeing and being seen are enjoyed equally as enriching aspects of being human. Revealing the most private feelings, thoughts, and behaviors is a source of satisfaction and joy as vulnerability allows for greater depths of knowing and accepting.

In such a family, people share eye contact frequently, muscle tonus has a resilient quality about it, movement responses are innovative and creative, and proxemics reflect feelings and attitudes regarding a specific interaction rather than defining the nature of a relationship.

Dysfunctional families commonly conspire to keep the truth from being know. Secrets about parentage, incest, or mental illness are skeletons in the closet that are guarded vigilantly. Withholding information or lying is a matter of course as they are attempts to maintain family myths, keep secrets, or stay out of trouble. People do not express their feelings, as they are afraid of humiliation and rejection. Vulnerability is seen as a weakness that opens the door to hurt. Telling the truth is considered foolish, bad, or crazy. Muscle tonus in this family is either flacid or overbounded as people attempt to inhibit their expression of feelings. Family members avert their gaze or stare someone down as they lie or withhold information. Redundant interactional patterns are safe in that they are known and therefore, diminish the opportunity for surprises and vulnerability.

Love. Family members in the evolutionary family feel loveable and loving. They also feel significant and competent. They trust themselves and each other, believe that they are being treated and treating each other fairly, and feel confident that each person is behaving in an open and honest manner. In this environment, love can come in. In truth and in love, the individual good and the collective good are synonomous. With such a feeling of abundance, joining is as satisfying as being joined, giving as receiving, yielding as directing, submitting as controlling, loving as being loved, and revealing as witnessing. In this family, each feeling, thought and behavior is a harmonious part of the whole. Each interaction allows for more unfolding, more becoming.

218

People in this family experience the same sense of fullness and wonder that you may experience when standing on a mountain peak, seeing a flower, watching a child play, or feeling water envelope your body. They feel unbounded and expansive. Every thought is accompanied by delight, every feeling by pleasure, every action by satisfaction. In the evolutionary family there is a sense of a promise fulfilled.

The dysfunctional family looks like a wasteland or a battlefield. In the wasteland, family members keep emotionally distant, are wary of each other and fearful that they will be undone. In the battlefield, family members are engaged in fighting in which they feel angry and hurt, resentful and disappointed that they are not feeling loved, lovable, or loving. Neither do people feel competent, or significant. In this family, the individual good and the common good are in continual conflict. With ths attitude of scarcity, joining is equivalent to loss of self, separating to abandoning, giving to blackmailing, receiving to indebting, yielding to giving in, directing to taking over, submitting to losing, controlling to winning, loving to mindreading, being loved to being given to, revealing to betraying, and witnessing to intruding.

In this family, members are not appreciated for the part they play in the whole. They do not feel that they have a choice, nor do they feel that they can make a difference in the family. Everyone clings tightly to what they have or desparately grabs for what they want. Playfulness or pleasant surprises are not found in the dysfunctional family. Change is experienced as threatening. Stability or sameness is safe in its familiarity. Personal growth is unheard of here, as it challenges the ethos of the family. The notion that the family could evolve creatively through its life cycle is never considered. The predominating feelings of hopelessness, fear, and animosity are often only masked by the facade of boredom. Without love, these people's bodies are lifeless with the look of a promise unfulfilled.

Theoretical Formulations

Methods of Identification of Dysfunctional and Evolutionary Behavior

Observation of Interactional Movement

The interactional dance is the focus of my attention as it is the key into the family's pain and ultimately to their healing. The what, how, when and where of each individual and various subsystems, in the context of the family as a whole is the source of my investigation. I look for movement patterns that do not get completed, that get stuck, diffused or diverted, that are highly charged affectively, and that are redundant. As I watch the patterns of the family dance, I notice the level at which family members are participating actively or passively, flexibly or rigidly, synchronously or asynchronously, and covertly or overtly. This information gives me information about how the family responds to stress and change.

Unstructured Movement

During every contact I have with the family, I observe the family dance to gather information about their functioning. How family members interact with each other in

the waiting room and when they leave the
office is as significant as their behavior
during the therapy session itself. During the
session, their casual behavior is again, as
significant as their behavior during
structured movement explorations. The various
aspects of movement behavior that I discussed
previously provide direction for me as the
family and I search for meaning and change.

Structured Movement Explorations

Structured movement explorations are the
tools with which I delve into the family
dance, searching for a road that leads the
family toward beneficial and satisfying
change. Examples of several of these
explorations are included later in this
section. There are four categories of
structured movement explorations, Diagnostic
Tasks, Translations, Awareness Processes, and
Therapist's Movement. Each best fits a
particular phase in the therapeutic process
though each may be adapted for a particular
purpose for use at any time.

Diagnostic Tasks are designed to help
the family and me identify the area of
interpersonal functioning which is associated
with the family's pain and to determine the
context in which the difficulty occurs (Bell,
1978). These loosely structured tasks allow
the family a great deal of improvisational
freedom. They are structured in such a way
that the family's salient issues emerge and
become visible. As such, Diagnostic Tasks are
used during the initial phase of therapy.

A Movement Scene Reenactment is often
one of the first structured explorations I
ask a family to do. It involves the use of
movement to depict a recurrent incident.

Milling is a Diagnostic Task in which family members move around the room in whatever way they want, making contact and interacting with whomever they desire. Dialoguing involves family members 'conversing' with each other without words, using only movement/dance. In Playing each individual takes a turn initiating movement play with one or more family members. Discovering is a type of Diagnostic Task in which family members set out to discover new movement options. In the Movement Web family members move continually together in a circle, holding hands to symbolize their emotional attachment. Used primarily to gather specific information about interactional patterns, the ICO Open Score allows family members the opportunity to explore conflictual issues in the areas of inclusion, control, and openness.

Translations are a category of structured movement explorations designed to clarify the interactional movement patterns in which the family is stuck, to ascertain areas of evolutionary behavior which can facilitate work toward solutions, and to create an environment in which the family can discover new behaviors. Translations are used from the beginning of therapy but become predominant as the family and I explore the subtleties of their painful interactional patterns.

There are two subtypes of Translations, Literal and Kinetic. Both translations provide the opportunity for family members to eloquently portray their emotional reality or a shared perception, thus adding depth to the verbal and feeling content of a session.

Literal Translations entail interpreting verbal metaphors such as, "We're like ships passing in the night". Kinetic Translations are more nebulous, in that family members use movement to portray an image, a feeling, or a sensation. Movement Doubling is a form of Kinetic Translation in which an individual uses movement to express what he or she perceives another person to be feeling. In Family Sculpting (Duhl, Kantor, and Duhl, 1973), family members place others in spacial arrangements and postures that express that person's perceptions. Still another type of Kinetic Translation, Family Choreography (Papp, 1976) entails generating an image, articulating it in a verbal metaphor, portraying the metaphor in movement, and then changing the movement to depict a desired outcome.

Awareness Processes are a third category of explorations that have to do with emphasizing what is occurring in the moment. Awareness Processes aid in deepening feelings which are present or emergent. They often work paradoxically, in that when family members are asked to do more of the same, something new emerges. For this reason, they are used in the middle and end phase of therapy predominantly.

Family Freeze, (Zenoff, 1979) involves the therapist stopping the action to point out a particular movement pattern that has emerged. This may occur during unstructured or structured movement explorations. Do and Exaggerate is an exploration in which the family is asked to continue the movement pattern they are doing and then to exaggerate it. In Role Reversal one family member assumes the movement of another family member temporarily. And, finally, in Practicing family members move with each other using new options discovered during therapy.

223

The fourth category of structured movement explorations is Therapist's Movement (Bell and Zenoff, 1980). As a catalyst for change, the therapist uses whatever possibilities exist to support the family in discovering, practicing, and integrating more coherent, efficient, and satisfying behavior. Here the therapist uses his or her own movement as an intervention.

As Unbalancer the therapist might move with a family member who needed support to maintain his or her position. As Anchorer the therapist might use physical contact to reinforce a new learning. Video is a mode in which the therapist uses movement to reflect back to the family what they are doing. As Model the therapist supports change by using movement to suggest alternatives.

Therapeutic Process

Family therapy in motion is a process of joining a family in their dance and helping them to find new steps. It means searching for doors into the family's pain as a way out. By exploring the intricate patterns of each family's dance, and by addressing the family's fear of change, the therapeutic process heightens the possibility for a new pattern. A new family dance emerges that allows each family member greater opportunity for becoming.

Phases in Family Therapy

A developmental sequence normally occurs in the course of family therapy. As therapy progresses, different goals, behaviors, attitudes, and feelings become predominant for the family, the therapist, and the system of interaction between the family and the therapist known as the family therapy system. Just as in any interpersonal system, whether issues in the area of inclusion, control, or openness take priority depends on the goal of each phase and the area of conflict in the family. Overlap is common however, since salient issues are present throughout therapy.

The Initial Phase

Therapy begins with the forming of a partnership between the family and myself. We must develop a system in which we can work together to identify the area in which the family's problem lies, inclusion, control, or openness, to reduce the family's pain, and to increase their coherence, efficiency, and satisfaction.

Therapist's Attitude During the Initial Phase.

From the moment of my first contact with a family, I form hunches about their behavior. My observing the family's behavior during unstructured and structured interactions, I collect information about their functioning. I attempt to identify the area in which their problem lies--inclusion, control, or openness. I sift through the vast array of information they present, trying to figure out how they are organized, what is bringing them pain, why they are stuck, and what will help them get unstuck. This becomes the basis for the systemic hypotheses that I formulate.

To deduce this information, I am especially aware of the interactional patterns in their family dance. I gather data about the family by continually observing them during random or unstructured movement

in the normal course of therapy. I also
create structured movement explorations that
elicit information about particular
interactional patterns in which they are
experiencing pain.

In the initial stage of family therapy,
I allow my senses and imagination free rein.
Without evaluating, I assimilate information
about the family, paying attention to the
interactions among family members and between
the family and me. I make no attempt to be
logical; ideas about the family system emerge
from my creative unconscious. I use my
sensitivity, imagination, creativity, and
ingenuity as I allow my senses the freedom to
explore, no matter how apparently illogical,
silly, or irrelevant. My hunches become
hypotheses that I later test and refine by
observing how the family responds to my
structured movement explorations.

Phase-Related ICO Issues During The
Initial Phase. Concurrent with my search for
redundant interactions and for roads into
those areas of conflict, is the process of
forming a partnership with the family. As in
any interpersonal system, inclusion issues
predominate initially. We must establish
feelings of belonging, find out who is a
member of our family therapy system, and
decide whether we share a common task. The
family's ambivalence about allowing me into
their system makes these issues all the more
poignant.

Yet joining is not simply a matter of
inclusion. The family therapy system exists
for the purpose of change. Issues of control
(such as who takes responsibility, who will
lead, how power will be exerted, and how
decisions will be reached) must be negotiated
if we are going to accomplish that purpose.

Control problems are exacerbated by the fact
that the family often defines the situation
and the task differently than I do. They
believe that one family member has a problem,
and they want me to "make that person
better"; I believe that the family as a whole
is stuck and that only the whole family can
find a satisfying solution.

Openness issues complicate the joining
process further. The family and the therapist
must find out how human, intimate, honest,
vulnerable, and transparent they can be
together. The family must experience the
therpaist's humanness and caring if they are
to develop the trust necessary to go deeply
into the problems that brought them to
therapy and find new solutions. The control
issues and openness issues between therapist
and family must be resolved if the family is
to let go of dysfunctional patterns and
discover new, more satisfying behaviors.
However, in order for the family and
therapist to join together as a coherent
working unit, the crucial issues remain those
of inclusion: developing a sense of
belonging, defining membership, and
experiencing committment.

The Middle Phase.

As the family and therapist become
joined together in a coherent system, the
therapist's focus shifts to that of
catalyzing change. My interventions are
designed to test my systemic hypotheses and
apply the results in an attempt to help the
family become "unstuck".

Therapist's Attitude During the Middle
Phase. It is essential to this phase of
investigation that I remain open to

perceiving the family's responss, whatever it might be. When family members behave in a way that does not fit my hypothesis, rather than attempting to fit the family into my hypothesis, I refine it. The family's interactions during these movement explorations show me and them more specifically where they are stuck and where there is flexibility. Spontaneous discoveries occur with amazing frequency during the movement process, as family members behave in an unexpected way, surprising themselves and their family.

Watching interactional movement patterns, I observe how the family regulates itself and how it strengthens or inhibits growth. I form conclusions about the validity of my hypothesis that I use to create movement interventions specifically designed to support family members in discovering new options and to stimulate the desired change. I use movement to place stress upon the family in such a way that it seeks a new way out of the discomfort. Alternatively, I may use movement to create situations that require new forms of behavior. As the family discovers new modes of interacting, I help the family to generalize from this incident in therapy to interactions in their daily lives.

My role is extremely active in this phase, as I am constantly attempting to evoke new behavior in the family by provoking, prodding, modeling, and inviting. As I threaten the family's stability, control issues predominate in the interaction between the family and myself.

Phase-Related ICO Issues During The Middle Phase. Change is a complex phenomenon that brings up a multitude of issues. The family must feel that our relationship is secure enough to weather the winds of change. They must be able to rely on me and my cotherapist when they feel despairing and afraid, and they must feel that we can help them find their way out of their stuckness and pain into more satisfying forms of interaction. Ostensibly, the family enters therapy to change, however, their ambivalence about change and their responses to their threatned stability bring control issues to the forefront. Paradoxically, they must let go and give up control before reorganization and change can occur. As therapist, I can only create conditions that foster change. Only the family itself creates change.

Yet issues of inclusion and openness are also addressed during the process of change. The family must feel that we belong to the same team, that they are full partners on that team, and that their well being is of primary importance. They must also know that they can have a life of their own, apart from us.

The family therapy system must also address the inclusion issue of boundaries between subsystems. The therapist is analogous to the parental subsystem and must be cognizant of maintaining appropriate boundaries. Whitaker (1982) discusses the danger of being absorbed by the family during this phase of therapy. "The therapist may become so comfortable and relaxed in the setting that he's like the parent who becomes one with the children. The therapy group is then a peer group rather than a two-generation unit and as such is dysfunctional" (p. 297).

If the family is to change and become more human with each other, openness issues such as intimacy, vulnerability, and honesty must be addressed during this phase. As a result of the therapist modeling vulnerability, the family gets support in risking the exposure of its raw nerves. Intimacy requires that both parties be vulnerable. The therapist aids the family in accepting change as a way of life by being sensitive to the primary issues of control and the secondary issues of inclusion and openness.

The End Phase

If the work has been successful to this point, the family begins to discover new ways of interacting with each other, structurally reorganizes, and starts to flow more smoothly, handling the stresses of daily life more easily and creatively. Spontaneous creative behavior often arises during sessions in this stage of therapy which require minimal intervention on my part.

Therapist's Attitude During the End Phase. In this final phase, I become more like a member of the stage crew than a director. I remain available and ready to support the family in whatever way they may need me as they practice their new behavior and integrate the changes into their more flexible and expanding repertoire.

This line of investigation and application forms the skeleton of my work with families. The stages overlap frequently as I am continually gathering information, forming hunches, testing my hypotheses, and applying the results. Attempts to get clarity about family interactions become interventions that affect the family and stimulate change. Every interaction between me and the family must therefore be regarded as therapeutic intervention.

Phase-Related ICO Issues During The End Phase. Entering the end phase, the family is more familiar with the process of change and is more flexible. Now the therapist must support the integration of changes and prepare for separation. In the process of integrating and separating, the family and the family therapy system reorganize. The therapist progressively takes a back stage role, while the family members practice their new behavior and become less reliant on the therapist. During this stage of therapy, the family initiates movement explorations on their own and begins to interact in a more flexible and creative way. Family members will frequently turn to me and ask if it is okay for them to put something into movement. On the other hand, a family member may spontaneously translate their feelings into movement while talking. Therapy sessions often begin with reports of spontaneous behavioral changes in the family during the week. I sometimes ask the family to demonstrate the new behavior by doing a Movement Scene Reenactment. In this way they take credit for and integrate the new behavior.

The therapist must relinquish control as the family assumes greater responsibility, taking initiative and risks, making mistakes and trying again. The therapist must feel good enough about him or herself that competence does not have to be sought through the assertion of leadership or the wielding of power.

As control issues are renegotiated between the family and the therapist, and the family experiences more success and joy,

231

their desire for autonomy becomes more pronounced. The therapist must let go of the family during this separation process, just as he or she merged with the family during the joining process. The therapist now is able to shift into a position of greater transparency and vulnerability, becoming representative of a model family member. Paradoxically, as the therapist and family become more intimate, separation can occur. In this final phase of therapy, when the family has achieved a greater degree of openness with each other and with the therapist, the family prepares to separate by first taking over leadership of the session and then by declaring their autonomy as a separate unit.

In successful therapy, the family's desire for openness is connected to feelings of increased lovability, feelings of appreciation for their uniqueness, and a desire for continued change and growth. Their willingness to assume more responsibility grows as they feel more competent and able to cope. Their desire for autonomy walks hand in hand with their feelings of belonging to their own family and trust in its coherence.

Table I summarizes the characteristics of each phase.

Table I

PHASE-RELATED ISSUES IN THE FAMILY THERAPY PROCESS

Family-Therapist System	Initial Phase	Middle Phase	End Phase
Family-Therapist Interaction			
Goal:	Joining Together	Instabiality & Change	Reorganization & Flexibility
Behavior:	Inclusion	Control	Openness
Family Attitude	Ambivalent about Changing	Eager to Discover & Explore	Intent on Integration & Practice
Therapist Activity	Gathering Information & Identifying Problem	Formulating, Testing, & Applying Hypotheses	Observing & Supporting of Results
Desirable Therapist Traits	Intuitive Sensitive Imaginativae	Rigorous Logical Comprehensive	Practical Generalizing Supportive
Therapist Role*	Detective	Catalyst	Supporter

*See Table II for elaboration.

233

Role of Therapist

Therapist's Use of Self Regarding Phase-Related Issues

Though interaction between the family and the therapist through the phases of family therapy follow the normal sequence of addressing the interpersonal dimensions of inclusion, control, and openness, the dimension comprising the focus of conflict may vary for different families. The therapist's use of self must be multifaceted if she or he is to be successful with a diversity of families in the process of joining together, catalyzing change, and supporting integration and reorganization. How I use myself depends on whether issues of inclusion, control, or openness are focal for the family and the family therapy system. I may function as a participant who moves with the family, a director who elicits movement from them, or a model moving while the family watches. As therapy progresses and the predominant issues change, my participation with the family also shifts. I become either a supporter moving with the family in an adjunctive role, a coach suggesting emergent movement possibilities, or a witness observing and reflecting movement back to the family.

Table II, the THERAPIST'S USE OF SELF IN PHASE RELATED ISSUES, depicts the various approaches that are assumed by the therapist, depending on the area of conflict in the family and family therapy system.

TABLE II

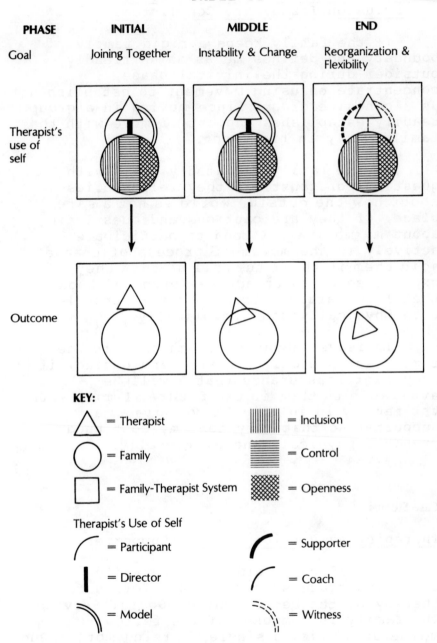

PHASE   INITIAL   MIDDLE   END

Goal   Joining Together   Instability & Change   Reorganization & Flexibility

Therapist's use of self

Outcome

KEY:

△ = Therapist

◯ = Family

▢ = Family-Therapist System

▥ = Inclusion

▤ = Control

▧ = Openness

Therapist's Use of Self

= Participant

= Director

= Model

= Supporter

= Coach

= Witness

Therapist as Participant and Supporter if Inclusion Issues are Conflictual

If the family keeps a rigid family boundary and defines me as an unfriendly outsider during the initital phase, I concentrate on using movement to establish us as a cohesive group. Since moving in a group readily establishes rapport, I move with the family early in treatment.

If the family repeatedly deals with questions of trust, if they tell stories about how the outside world is not a safe place, if they are cautious and questioning about my motives, I tend to participate actively in the movement process of change. I join them in their turmoil so that they experience me as an active force and know that I am participating in their struggle both physically and symbolically.

If issues about my commitment to the family surface while we are terminating, if they want reassurance that I will be available to them in the future, I move with the family in an adjunctive role as a supporter so that they feel my continued presence physicaly and emotionally.

Case Studies

Therapist as Participant and Supporter

The Allens, a blue collar family receiving state support, was referred for therapy by the Department of Social Services. The family is composed of the following members: Gloria, a single, working mother who gave birth to her oldest daughter out of wedlock and gave birth to another daughter and son while married to a military man. She feels lonely, unable to make friends, and pressured by money problems. Bob, her fourteen-year-old son, has recently rejoined the family after being in a group home for two years. He refuses to go to school, do household chores, or maintain his personal hygiene. Betty, Gloria's eighteen-year-old daughter, has repeated her mother's story, having just had a baby out of wedlock. She has no money, lives with her baby in the mother's home, and wants her mother to take care of her baby while she spends time with her friends. Dottie, the younger daughter, is thirteen years old. She has just been expelled from school for bashing a teacher's head against a wall after the teacher told her to return to her classroom. Dottie is identified as the good kid in the family who does anything Mom wants her to do, Betty is Mom's best friend and confidante, and Bob is the identified patient (IP) and the cause of the family's problem. The family's presenting complaint was that Bob was neither doing his chores nor attending school.

As the initial interview began, the family was reserved and aloof. They talked about how unsafe their neighborhood was and how dangerous the world was in general. The family stated that everything had been fine when Bob was away, but now the house was crowded, with Bob sleeping on the living room sleeper sofa. I and my cotherapist, Michael, suggested that Betty and her baby move elsewhere, to which Gloria responded that though she did not want to take care of her daughter's baby, she did not want Betty to leave the house, as her eldest daughter was her only confidante. No matter how we approached the family, we were met by the idea that Bob was the problem and he was the one who needed changing.

To begin to shift the family's definition of the problem from one of blame to one of systemic awareness, I asked the family to do a Diagnostic Task that I call The Movement Web. This movement exploration also gives me the opportunity to join the family in movement and gather information about the conflictual issues in their family system.

To begin The Movement Web, I had the family stand in a circle and hold hands to symbolize their familial attachment to each other. I asked someone to move, without specifying who. After stopping the action and bringing the family's awareness to the movement they had just participated in (though they may not have initiated it directly), I asked them to move again without stopping. Once again I stopped them and we talked about how everything that happens to one family member affects the entire family. After moving and stopping again, I questioned them about who was leading and who was following the movement. The movement pattern was so complex by this time, it was not surprising that each of them responded with a different name. Without specifying who, I asked someone to go off balance during the next movement trial. Suddenly, Gloria turned to me and spontaneously asked, "Is this about letting go of and holding onto my kids?" The remainder of the session was spent talking about this issue and exploring it in movement by having them do a Kinetic Translation in which each demonstrated what holding on and letting go felt like for him or her.

The following week, at the request of Dottie, the thirteen-year-old daughter, we did the Movement Web again. This time Michael and I joined them. When the action became quite vigorous, with continual pushing and

238

pulling, Dottie said to her mother, who was next to her, "You are always resisting me!" Again, the theme of accommodating and resisting became the focus for the session. I continued to work with movement, using the Diagnostic Task called ICO Open Score. I asked the family members to take turns leading and following each other, and I had the leaders tell their partner whether the partner was going with or resisting their direction. Bob, who rarely spoke more than monosyllables, began to prompt his mother, saying, "You're holding back a little...that's better...good." Gloria had a difficult time letting go and following, whereas Bob was quite accommodating and responsive. Dottie and Bob began resisting each other, and when Dottie tried to trick Bob by suddenly stopping, they both went flying in the direction of the resistance.

By actively participating in The Movement Web with the family, Michael and I physically and symbolically joined the family dance. At the same time that the family's salient issues emerged, they relaxed, became more animated and interacted together positively. Following each movement exploration, they spontaneously talked about how this theme was manifested in their daily life.

During the movement and the subsequent discussions, I noticed a decrease in an interactional pattern that frequently occurred between Gloria and Bob and sometimes between other family members and him. Gloria would ask Bob a question and he would remain quiet, looking back at her with glass eyes as if he were seeing through her. Then he would shrug his shoulders, saying, "I don't know." The more Bob was interrogated, the glassier his eyes became, the more nonchalant his

239

shrug became, the more passive he became, and the more he seemingly retreated into himself. The mother, or whoever was involved with Bob, would give up with a sigh of frustration and turn to me and Michael with a helpless look.

After seeing the family several times, Michael began a similar interrogation technique with Bob. The more distant and passive Bob became, the more annoyed and insistent Michael became. As each became more entrenched in his respective attitude, the tension in the room mounted. I decided to illustrate this interactional pattern via a Kinetic Translation. I saw that Bob closed up more tightly as first his mother and now as Michael attempted to open him up through questioning. I explained that I wanted each of us to take a turn closing up and staying as tight as we might while others tried to open us up. I told them they could do anything they wanted short of hurting themselves or another person. Upon hearing my direction, Bob looked at me in disbelief and asked, "You mean I'm not supposed to let them open me up?" When I responded affirmatively, his eyes twinkled and a slight smile crept onto his lips.

I suggested that Michael and his mother try to open Bob first. Gloria immediately began to tickle Bob, who, amid gales of laughter, remained as tight as a clam. Gloria exclaimed several times, "God, you are strong!" She turned to me and said, "This is how I feel at the time when I am trying to get him to do chores around the house." Working together, Michael and Gloria could not open him up until Gloria tickled him relentlessly. Each of us took a turn doing the closing and the opening until everyone felt satisfied. In an animated and poignant outpouring, Gloria revealed that she had been wishing often that Bob had not come back home and that she wanted to send him back to the group home. She was feeling that he was too much trouble, that he never wanted to do any of the housework, that she had to pay more money for food, and that she had to cook much more when he was there. For her, it would be much easier if he were not there. As Gloria told this to Bob, her face and body softened and opened, her eyes moistened, and her gaze was steady and soft. Bob's reaction was equally touching as he talked about feeling like an outsider in the family and at school. He remained energized and open as he talked. By making overt what had been covert, the interactional pattern changed. Paradoxically, by exaggerating the existing pattern, there was a deepening of feelings, and change spontaneously occurred.

The family did not return to therapy. However, a phone conversation with Gloria revealed that Bob was going to school, doing his household chores, and maintaining his personal hygiene. Without being told to, he had shaved for the first time in several weeks. The presenting problem was no longer an issue for the family, and Gloria felt no need to return to therapy. In a follow-up call three weeks later, Gloria remarked that "Things were fine and Bob was going to school and doing his chores. Betty and the baby were living at home and Dottie was back in school."

Therapist as Director and Coach if Control Issues are Conflictual

If control issues are predominant in the initial formation of the family therapy system, I use movement to clarify who is in charge. In the first session, I may direct family members to do a variety of movement explorations in which I set the stage and observe their interactions.

Control problems tend to prevail in the middle phase of therapy. For instance, the family may want me and my cotherapist to inititate and be responsible for change. In such a case, I take on the role of director/coach, supporting them in their search for new options. I become less active, yet still available; communicating symbolically and literally that the family has the responsibility for change.

If the family members question their competence and their ability to handle situations that may arise after termination, I pull back even more, becoming a coach who merely suggests ways in which they could explore their new found skills. My coaching interventions are frequently suggestions such as, "How might you work on this issue in movement?"

My work with the Laird family portrays the therapist as director and coach.

The cast of characters in this family included the mother, Sarah, who was in her middle thirties and finishing her undergraduate degree in pre-medicine; her ten year old daughter, Susie, who was about ten pounds overweight and wore a pout on her face; and the mother's boyfriend and housemate of three years, Dave, who taught preschool age children. The presenting problem was that the boyfriend was trying to break up the mother/daughter relationship. Within the first minutes of the initial therapy session, Dave attempted to direct the session by shooting questions at Sarah and then responding for her. As a means of establishing leadership during the joining process and of gathering information about the family's interactional patterns, I asked them to do a Kinetic Translation.

I asked Dave to use movement to symbolically show how he was attempting to join Sarah and Susie. He directed Sarah and Susie to remain sitting next to each other on the large pillows on the floor, and he stood up in front of them. He then proceeded to dive between them, separating them with his hands and trying to put his face between theirs. Sarah immediately shrieked, "This is exactly how it feels! Like you're trying to break us apart!"

In response to Dave's disclaimer that his first attempt did not accurately depict his intentions, I asked him to try again using a different approach. The second time, he again left Sarah and Susie sitting close to each other on the pillows. He stood up once again, spread his arms wide, and advanced toward them, gathering them in his arms in a big hug so that he had the two of them in a tight embrace. This time Sarah said with anger and disgust, "Now I feel suffocated."

I then asked Sarah if she would portray how she would like him to join the family. She created the following scene: She and her daughter stood side by side in the middle of the room. She noticed and remarked that she was much taller than Susie, her ten year old daughter, so she knelt down so that they would be approximately the same height. She then showed Dave how she wanted him to approach. She had him face the two of them from a distance of about six feet, kneel, and move toward them on his knees until he was about two feet away, directly in front of them. All three of them kept their arms at their sides throughout the scene.

Needless to say, these Kinetic Translations provided rich material for hypotheses about the family system. Michael and I began formulating hunches about boundary problems between the mother and daughter and power and leadership problems between the mother and her boyfriend.

Weeks later, another session began with an argument about Sarah's reaction to Dave's initiation of affection. He argued that whenever he approached her she pushed him away and either blamed him for something, accused him of wanting something from her, or made a sarcastic and caustic remark. Dave explained that he typically at this point responded in kind and a full fledged argument would ensue, ending in an angry separation. Sarah denied this and defended herself by saying that when he truly offered affection, she eagerly accepted it. In fact, according to Sarah, Dave rarely volunteered the gifts of affection that she desired such as massages.

I asked them to put the interaction in question into movement using a Movement Scene Reenactment. The two of them agreed on a sequence that proceeded like this: Sarah and Dave stood looking at each other from about a distance of six feet. Dave stretched out his arm, with his palm rotated upward as he walked toward Sarah. By the time he began to put his arm around her shoulder, Sarah had already stiffened and retreated in her head, neck, and spine. She looked suspiciously at Dave and backed away, angry, hurt, and pouting. He stood there, frustrated and fuming.

As this was our reentry into the issue of Dave's style of approach, I asked Dave to begin to explore new ways of approaching Sarah by doing a Diagnostic Task that I call Discovering. I asked Sarah to focus on her somatic responses and any feelings or thoughts that emerged as Dave moved toward her, and I asked her to verbalize what she was experiencing. In doing this, she became aware that she assumed that Dave wanted something from her and that she was obligated to respond to his desire. Her stiffening was an attempt to fend off his request and her feelings of guilt for not responding as she felt she should.

This brought us into Sarah's emotional reality. Her current experience was related to a dream that she had recounted and expressed in movement during a prior session. In this dream, Sarah is in a forest at sunset with eight younger children for whom she is responsible. The children are nowhere to be seen, and she is frightened that she will not be able to find them before the sun goes down. Her feeling in the dream is one of fear and despair that she will not be able to act responsibly. In enacting the dream sequence, Sarah closed her eyes and reached gropingly into the space around her, as if in a gossamer web. She tentatively moved in a circle around herself, then opened her eyes and dropped her arms. This dream symbolized the burdensome feelings of responsibility that Sarah always carried with her. The eight children in the woods remained a metaphor throughout therapy for her feelings of shouldering too much responsibility.

Sarah became aware that her
interpretation of Dave's approach (that he
wanted something from her) was based on her
feelings of being overburdened with
responsibility. This insight did not change
her feelings or her suspicions. It did,
however, allow her to begin asking him to
approach in specific ways so that she would
clearly perceive his movement as a
demonstration of affection rather than as a
request for her to do something.

This use of Discovering allowed Sarah
and Dave to find a new way of making contact
with each other. In the context of their
relationship, they explored Sarah's emotional
reality, fluidly moving between her private
world and their family dance. This provided
them with an experience of effective and
satisfying problem solving. Rather than blame
and accuse each other as they were wont to
do, they took responsibility as a team to
change an interaction they both considered to
be problematic. As a team, they found a new
dance.

Therapist as Model and Witness if Openness Issues are Conflictual

If openness issues such as vulnerability
are predominant in the formation of the
family therapy system, I use my movement to
create an atmosphere of acceptance. I might
use movement to express a feeling I am having
regarding the family, my cotherapist, or my
own family. By my own movements, I make the
process of becoming transparent and
vulnerable safer and less mysterious.

During the middle phase of therapy, if
family members constantly feel afraid of
risking exposure, I support their process by

taking risks myself, using movement to model intimacy and express my appreciation of each person's uniqueness. I might offer someone a back rub or a foot massage, wrestle playfully with a child, or stretch out and relax as a way of inviting the family to loosen up and let their hair down.

If the family continues to be skeptical about appreciating the uniqueness of each family member, remains fearful about being transparent, I function as a witness, reflecting back to them their movement behavior. As we separate, I function more like a model family member, using my movement to show how I am feeling about the impending separation or about something in my personal family situation. In this way, the family experiences my vulnerability and takes that experience with them when therapy terminates.

Examples of therapist model and witness follow with the Tannen family.

Paul, the father of the Tannen family, worked for a large computer corporation and was in the process of resolving the property settlement from the divorce of his second marriage. Two children from a previous marriage lived with him part-time. His thirteen-year-old daughter, Cheryl, preferred to stay at her mother's house but was quite vocal about wanting a more intimate relationship with her father. His ten-year-old son, Billy, who identified with his dad, had been tested for reading problems that were determined to be due to emotional stress. The testing psychologist suggested the family seek therapy.

In the first interview, Paul talked about some of the problems he was experiencing regarding his property settlement. He was apparently in great distress over the separation and the subsequent legal battle, but he was not inclined to talk about his feelings. The children reported that Dad never told them how he felt and that they both wanted to know, as they were affected by his moods whether he said anything about them or not.

After Paul made a feeble, intellectualized attempt at explaining what he was experiencing, I stepped in as his Movement Double. I asked Paul to watch me move and then to tell me what he felt as he watched. I used the movement that was emergent in his body posture as the basis for my movement. I let my chest collapse, my head hang, and my body sway to express some of the sadness and dejection I perceived in his attitude. My arms tensed and my hands formed fists and flailed the air in short, quick strokes of frustration. Paul immediately said that my movement evoked the quality of his feelings--sadness, anger, despair, and perplexity. When I asked Paul to find movements of his own to express his feelings, he stood with his feet more than shoulder width apart, his chest retreated and collapsed, and his head and arms hanging. With his hands clenched in fists, he raised his arms in an arclike movement in front of him until they were extended above his head. At the same time, he arched his back, threw his head back, and grimaced. He remained extended in that position for several seconds and then collapsed to his sunken standing posture with a loud sigh. Paul then began to express some of the feelings of frustration and failure he was experiencing. Both of the children felt relieved at seeing and hearing about their father's feelings. They began asking him questions about himself and talking about their feelings for him. The rest of the session focused on Paul's attitudes about expressing his feelings in front of his children and their desire to spend more time with him and to get to know him better. The dreaded consequences of openness did not follow Paul's revelation of vulnerable parts of himself. Rather, his expression of feelings paved the road to greater intimacy among him and his children.

During a session in the middle phase of therapy, Cheryl and Billy complained that their Dad was uptight most of the time. Only when he was on vacations did he hang loose. Even after the children described in detail how his 'uptight' behavior differed from his "hang loose" behavior, Paul remained unconvinced of the validity of their perceptions. Moreover, he could not understand how they could think that about him.

Michael then asked all three of them to draw two pictures each, one of Dad "uptight" during work days and one of Dad "hanging loose" during vacations. All three of their "uptight" pictures were significantly different from their respective "hang loose" drawings. Paul's "uptight" drawing was red and angular. His "hang loose" drawing was blue and curvaceous.

Since one of our aims was to encourage the Tannens to openly express their feelings toward each other, I asked them to put their drawings into movement. Paul first translated the red, "uptight" drawing. He stiffened his body and moved exclusively in straight lines in the sagital plane, very much like a robot. Transitions were abrupt and direct. He gazed straight ahead. Then he enacted the blue, "hang loose" drawing. His body softened and relaxed, and he occasionally lay down in a

languid, casual repose on the floor. He
smiled and made eye contact with everyone in
the room. His movement was sustained and his
transitions were smooth.

I suggested that we all get up and
together, move Paul's red drawing and his
blue drawing. The children were eager to do
that. As you might imagine, no one looked at
anyone else or made any contact whatsoever
during the red drawing enactment. We were
like machines, powered by an outside force,
unaware of our surroundings. The blue drawing
found us lounging together, smiling at each
other, and making physical contact and eye
contact.

After we moved both drawings, Paul began
to talk about his feelings of relaxation on
vacations and his feelings of pressure and
responsibility when he is working. As Paul
shared his conflicts with his children, they
were able to empathize and offer creative
suggestions, such as hanging a sign on his
door which said, "Red: Do Not Disturb." The
discussion had an intimate quality about it
with each family member talking about his or
her feelings while the others listened and
responded. "The Red and the Blue" became a
metaphor for how Dad and the kids were
interacting together. In the final phase of
therapy, Cheryl or Billy often reminded Paul
to be blue when he was at home with them,
even if he chose to be red at work. The
translation of Paul's drawings into movement
provided a road into a painful interactional
pattern in the family dance and became a
vehicle for change.

Bibliography

Aponte, H., "Underorganization in the Poor
    Family," P. Guerin, ed. Family Therapy:
    Theory and Practice. New York: Gardner
    Press, 1976.

Ashby, W.R. Design for a Brain. 2nd Ed.,
    London: Chapman and Hall, 1960.

Bateson, Gregory. Mind and Nature: A
    Necessary Unity. New York: E.P. Dutton.
    1978.

_____. Steps to an Ecology of Mind. New York:
    Ballatine, 1972.

Bell, J. "Families on the Move," Presentation
    at the Annual Conference for the
    American Dance Therapy Association,
    Philadelphia, 1979.

_____ and Zenoff, N. "Family Dance Therapy."
    Presentation to Stockton Family Therapy
    Group, Stockton, California, 1980.

Birdwhistell, R.L. Introduction to Kinesics.
    Louisville, Ky.: University of
    Louisville Press, 1952.

_____. Kinesics and Context. Philadelphia:
    University of Pennsylvania Press, 1971.

Bowen, M., Family Therapy in Clinical
    Practice. New York: Jason Aronson, 1978.

Colangelo, N. and W. Doherty. "The Family
    FIRO Model: Implications for
    Conceptualizing Family Issues, Assigning
    Treatment Priorities, and Selecting
    Suitable Therapies", Presented at the
    American Association for Marriage and
    Family Therapy Annual Conference,
    Dallas, Texas, 1982.

Condon, William S. "Cultural Microrhythms,"
    Interaction Rhythms. Martha Davis, ed.,
    New York; Human Sciences Press, Inc.,
    1982.

Dell, P.F. "Beyond Homeostasis: Toward a
    Concept of Coherence", Family Process
    21, (March 1982), 21-41.

_____. "Interpersonal Components of Change and
    Failure to Change", unpublished
    manuscript.

_____. "From Systemic to Clinical
    Epistemology: From Bateson to Maturana,"
    Presented to the Seventh International
    Symposium of the Institut fuer Ehe und
    Familie, Zurich, Switzerland, 1981.

_____. and Harold Goolishian. "Order Through
    Fluctuation: An Evolutionary
    Epistemology for Human Systems."
    Australian Journal of Family Therapy,
    2:4, 175-184.

Dulicai, D. "Non-Verbal Assessment of Family
    System," Arts Psychotherapy. 1977, 4
    (2), 55-62.

Duhl, B. From the Inside Out and Other
    Metaphors. New York: Brunner/Mazel,
    1983.

Duhl, F.J., Kantor, D. and Duhl, B.S. "Learning, Space and Action in Family Therapy: A Primer of Sculpture," in D. Block (Ed.). Techniques of Family Psychotherapy. New York: Grune and Stratton, 1973.

Elkaim, Mony. "Non-Equilibrium, Chance, and Change in Family Therapy," Journal of Marital and Family Therapy, 291-297, July 1981.

Ford, F., Herrick, J. "Family Rules: Family Life Styles," American Journal of Orthopsychiatry, 44 (1), January 1974.

Haley, J. Strategies of Psychotherapy. New York: Grune and Stratton, 1963.

_____. "Toward a Theory of Pathological Systems," in Watzlawick, P. and Weakland, J., (eds.), The Interactional View. New York: W.W. Norton, 1977.

Hall, E. The Silent Language. New York: Doubleday, 1959.

_____. The Hidden Dimension. New York: Doubleday, 1966.

Doubler, M. Dance, A Creative Art Experience. Madison: University of Wisconsin Press, 1957.

Hoffman, Lynn. Foundations of Family Therapy. New York: Basic Book, Inc., 1981.

Jackson, D. "The Question of Family Homeostasis," Psychiatric Quarterly Supplement, 31:79-90, 1957.

Kestenberg, J. The Role of Movement Patterns
    in Development I. New York: Dance
    Notation Bureau Press, 1977.

Laban, R. The Mastery of Movement. Second
    Edition. Revised and enlarged by Lisa
    Ullman. London: MacDonald and Evans,
    1960.

Lamb. W. Body Code. London: Routledge & Kegan
    Paul Ltd., 1979.

Lamb, W. Posture and Gesture. London: Gerald
    Duckworth & Co. Ltd., 1965.

Leath, A.A., "Manifesto for a New Theater, or
    Essays Celebrating Myself." Creative
    Behavior and Artistic Development in
    Psychotherapy, American Psychological
    Association, Sept. 5, 1967.

Minuchin, S. et al. Families of the Slums.
    New York: Basic Books, 1969.

____. Families and Family Therapy. Cambridge,
    Mass.: Harvard University Press, 1974.

____ and H. Charles Fishman. Family Therapy
    Techniques. Cambridge: Harvard
    University Press, 1981.

Moore, C.L. Executives in Action. London:
    MacDonald and Evans, 1982.

Napier, A. with Whitaker, C. The Family
    Crucible. New York: Harper and Row,
    1978.

Neill, J. Kniskern, D. From Psych to System:
    The Evolving Therapy of Carl Whitaker.
    New York: The Guilford Press, 1982.

Papp, P. "Family Choreography," in P. Guerin (Ed.). Family Therapy. Theory and Practice. New York: Gardner, 1976.

_____ and Silverstein, O., and Carter, E. "Family Sculpting in Preventive Work with 'well Families'," Family Process, 1973, 12:2, 197-212.

Prigogine, I. From Being to Becoming. San Francisco, Calif.: W.H. Freeman and Co., 1980.

Prigogine, I., Allen, P., and Herman, R., "The Evolution of Complexity and the Laws of Nature". In E. Laszlo and J. Bierman. (eds.), Goals for Mankind. Report to the Club of Rome, Vol. 1, Studies on the Conceptual Foundations, 1977.

Ramsden, P. Top Team Planning. London: Associated Business Programmes Ltd., 1973.

Reiss, David. The Family's Construction of Reality. Cambridge, Massachusetts: Harvard University Press, 1981.

Sagan, J.B., "On Founding a New Profession, the Creative Behavior Teacher, Creative Behavior and Artistic Development in Psychotherapy, American Psychological Association, Sept. 5, 1967.

Satir, V. Conjoint Family Therapy. Palo Alto: Science and Behavior Books, 1967.

_____. Peoplemaking. Palo Alto: Science and Behavior Books, 1972.

Schutz, W. FIRO: A Three Dimensional Theory
of Interpersonal Behavior. New York:
Rinehart and Co., Inc., 1958.

____. Profound Simplicity. San Diego:
University Associates, Inc., 1979.

____. The Human Element. Berkeley: Ten Speed
Press, In Press.

Speer, D.C. "Family Systems: Morphostasis and
Morphogenesis, or "Is Homeostasis
Enough?'" Family Process. 9:259-278,
1970.

Watzlawick, P., D. Jackson, and J. Beavin.
Pragmatics of Human Communication. New
York: W.W. Norton, 1967.

Wynne, L.C. et. al. "Pseudo-Mutuality in the
Family Relations of Schizophrenics,"
Archives of General Psychiatry 9 (1963),
161-206.

Zenoff, N. Personal Communications, Atherton,
California, 1979.

Zukav, Gary. The Dancing Wu Li Masters. New
York: William Morrow and Company, 1979.

Chapter 4

Experiential Movement Psychotherapy*

*Erma Dosamantes-Alperson, Ph.D., ADTR***

Genesis

As I considered what led me to regard dance/movement as a potential therapeutic modality and later to use it as an integral part of my work as a psychotherapist, I began to recollect many personal experiences, including personal contacts with admired and respected teachers and clinicians whose ideas molded my own thinking.

Moving from Mexico to the United States as a youngster without the advantage of knowing or speaking the English language literally caused me to feel like a "stranger in a strange land." I found refuge in modern dance at Henry Street. There I discovered that through improvisational movement I could express myself most clearly and directly,

**Dr. Dosamantes-Alperson is Professor and Director of the Graduate Movement Therapy Program at U.C.L.A. She is a clinical psychologist and a movement psychotherapist in private practice in Los Angeles.

without need for words. Modern dance teachers such as Murray Louis and Alwin Nikolais and later Beatric Seckler, Betty Osgood and Joyce Trissler taught me a great deal about the joy of dancing as a creative and a transformational experience.

As an undergraduate at the City University of New York, I became fascinated with psychology particularly with psychoanalytic theory. I recalled reading all of Freud's collected papers in one semester. To this day, I value this approach to the study of psychodynamics. Theoretical concepts derived from instinct theory, ego psychology and object relations theory have broadened my theoretical understanding as a psychotherapist.

As a doctoral student at Michigan State University during the sixties, I learned to appreciate the scientist-practitioner model for training clinicians. To date I continue to be attracted to this training model because it values equally intuition and intellect and does not treat them as polar opposites. Bert Karon, one of my psychology teachers who best exemplifies this model for me, became someone to emulate as a clinician.

While at Michigan State another teacher, Bill Kell, taught me the most important lesson I have learned about being a psychotherapist: that the "key" to knowing as a therapist has to do with empathically perceiving and reflecting back a client's own situation as s/he experinces or lives it. In this respect, the work of Carl Rogers has afforded me the most meaningful understanding of what an experiential therapeutic relationship is. From Gene Gendlin I have learned that clients can derive personal

258

meaning by focusing on their bodily-felt
experiencing.

Thomas Szasz' convincing arguments
against medical labeling and involuntary
commitment practices along with Ronald
Laing's regression-reintegration work with
individuals labeled "schizophrenic," forced
me to reevaluate my views of the medical
model and of the "treatment" offered at most
medical institutions to regressed
individuals.

Following graduate school I returned to
New York City to work at Hillside and
Elmhurst psychiatric hospitals and to
practice verbal psychotherapy privately. The
following year I became Director of
Counseling at the State University of New
York in Stony Brook and taught clinical
courses in psychology at the City University
of New York in Queens. During this period I
became acquainted with the work of Fritz
Perls who impressed me with his emphasis on
nonverbal expressive behavior. However, I
felt something lacking in Gestalt therapy. As
a dancer I realized that one could express
one's experience beyond the gestural level--
so I set out to search for ways of "moving
experience." I spent the following year at
U.C.L.A. studying dance therapy with Alma
Hawkins. Alma taught me how to shape or give
form to my internal experiencing through
spontaneous movement. She provided me with a
bridge between my training as a modern dancer
and as a psychologist.

Following this period I returned to
teach in clinical graduate psychology
programs at the University of Northern
Colorado and at California State University
in Los Angeles. At these schools I introduced
several experiential courses in "movement

259

psychotherapy." I also discovered the value
of imagery in psychotherapy through the work
of Joe Shorr, Jerry Singer, Mardi Horowitz
and Jesse Geller.

More recently as a practitioner and
teacher of dance/movement therapy I have felt
a need to evolve a theoretical framework
which makes sense to me and a way of working
that is congruent with my own clinical
observations. In this endeavor I have found
my special relationships with Burt Alperson
and Hedda Bolgar and the feedback of my
clients, graduate students and colleagues, to
be of immeasurable value.

Theoretical Model

The Experiencing or Phenomenal Self

How we function in any given situation
is dependent on how we perceive ourselves in
relation to the situation (Combs, Richards
and Richards, 1976). The phenomenal or
perceived self is the most important complex
of differentiations we make in our lives. It
is the central core of our being around which
all perceptions, conscious and unconscious,
are organized; it becomes the reference point
for everything we do.

To have a "self" refers to the
experience of being a distinct and conscious
entity. It encompasses the belief that we
possess a unique set of personality
characteristics, values and perceptions. This
belief allows us to maintain a sense of
continuity, consistency and stability that
makes dealing with an incomprehensible world
tolerable.

Origins of the Phenomenal Self

The phenomenal self evolves and is shaped by a spiraling series of interactions with our environment; the most powerful and influential of these involve emotionally significant others in our lives. Among the earliest differentiations infants make are those concerned with the definition of "me" and "not me." As physical beings children explore their surroundings through their senses and actions (Kestenberg, 1975; Piaget, 1930). In the process they discover their distinctiveness from others and things around them. They learn that all within the confines of their skin is "me" while all that lies outside it is "not me" (Mahler, Pine and Bergman, 1975; Schilder, 1950; Werner, 1957).

As childrens' capacity to conjure up and maintain mental images about themselves and others develops, they gain the confidence to explore their world with increased security even in the absence of their parents (Fairbairn, 1964; Jacobson, 1954; Klein, 1932; Piaget, 1930). The further acquisition of verbal language provides them with a shorthand through which to objectify and to share their experience explicitly with others (Bruner, 1964; Werner and Kaplan, 1964).

The phenomenal self is a social product evolving out of experience with people. Most significant and fundamental facts about ourselves are learned from what Sullivan (1947) called reflected appraisals, inferences about ourselves made as a consequence of feedback obtained from others. No experience in our development of a phenomenal self is as important nor has as far-reaching effects as the earliest experience within our families; while our

261

families themselves are the products and conveyors of the culture in which they exist.

For children to experience themselves as all right they must not only feel comfortable with their own bodies but also must possess an inner feeling of closeness to and acceptance from their primary caretakers. Parenting requires an adequate response to the phase specific needs of the child. If it is insufficient, inconsistent or excessive it will interfere with the child's emotional, social and intellectual development (Blanck and Blanck, 1979; Mahler, 1968). Our families provide us with the earliest opportunities to experience our sense of worth and adequacy.

As we proceed through childhood, adolescence, adulthood and senescence we encounter different sets of expectations and demands from others. How effectively we mediate issues having to do with self worth, dependency, autonomy, gender-identity, competence, competition, envy, sexuality, intimacy, responsibility, creativity, and death as well as the expression of modulation of our emotions, will greatly influence others' perceptions of us, our self-regard and the kinds of emotional adjustments we are able to make in different social situations (Erikson, 1950; Sullivan, 1947).

Perceiving and Processing Experience

At any given moment, the things we are able to perceive are almost limitless, yet we do not perceive in random fashion but select from the possibilities which are available to us (Ornstein, 1972). Merton (1948) used the term self-fulfilling prophecy to describe how once we are locked into a perception of what we are and what we are not, it becomes difficult for us to alter this perception and in fact we act to confirm it.

When confronted with any new situations, we deal with them in any of three ways (Combs et al, 1976). The experience may be (a) perceived, symbolized and organized in some relationship to the phenomenal self; (b) ignored because there is no perceived relationship to the self; (c) denied symbolization or given distorted symbolization because the experience is inconsistent with our self perception.

While change in the self's structure is possible, any major change whether it is prompted by external events or is self-initiated will be resisted because it will be experienced as disruptive and disorganizing to our integrity and security (Sullivan, 1947). Any incongruity between our felt experince at our self perception or between our self perception and a significant other's perception of us, will be perceived as a threat, experienced as an emotional conflict and responded to with tension and anxiety (Freud, 1959; Rogers, 1951). When emotionally threatened we tend to narrow our perceptual field as well as the range of expressive modes we use to symbolize our experience (Horowitz, 1978; Dosamantes-Alperson, 1983).

Organizing Experience Through Action and Receptive Modes

Our perceptions are organized around two modes of biological and psychological organization: an action and a receptive mode (Deikman, 1976). Field (1952) referred to these modes of perceiving as narrow and wide attending respectively. She described narrow attending as an automatic way of perceiving, reminiscent of the "questing beast" while wide attending occurred when the questing purposes where held in abeyance and there was no need to select one environmental event over another, making it possible to look at "the whole at once."

According to Deikman (1976) the receptive mode or wide attending mode prevails in early infancy and is organized for maximal intake from the environment. In this mode parasympathetic nervous activity and sensory-perceptual activity predominate. This mode soon is overriden by the action or narrow attending mode which originates with our need for biological survival and is oriented toward the manipulation of objects in the environment. In this mode sympathetic nervous system activity, striate muscle activity and goal-oriented activity assume eminence.

When emotoinally threatened we may narrow our perceptual field to such an extent that we may be unable to perceive more than one kind of response as available to us despite its inappropriateness. Narrowed perception makes it difficult for us to conceive of better and more effective solutions to problems.

Symbolizing Experience Through
Enactive, Image and Lexical Modes

We can also limit what we perceive by limiting the number of ways we use to represent or symbolize our experience. As human beings we have access to three ways of representing or symbolizing our experience: enactive, image and lexical (Bruner, 1964; Horowitz, 1972).

Meaning is expressed enactively through muscle tensions and action tendencies or incipient body movements (Horowitz, 1972). Therefore, this mode is best for conveying concepts of shape, direction and force. Individual enactive expressions may be tracked by observing the form, direction and emotional intensity displayed by the person while gesturing, posturing and moving (Dosamantes-Alperson and Merrill, 1980; Dosamantes-Alperson, 1983).

Meaning provided by the image mode is conveyed through the various sensory modalities (e.g., visual, auditory, tactile, etc.). Visual images are useful for parallel or simultaneous processing of information (Horowitz, 1972). This characteristic of visual images allows an individual to access past, present and future events simultaneously and to contemplate physically absent objects in relationship to one another, comparing them with respect to similarities and differences.

In the lexical mode, meaning is communicated through words. Because words are specialized for sequential processing, this mode facilitates conceptualization, analytical reasoning and abstract generalizations making detachment and objectivity possible (Horowitz, 1972). Through this mode one's private nonverbal experience may be made explicit via the consensually accepted symbols of verbal language (Dosamantes-Alperson, 1974).

Each representational mode possesses unique organizational properties which contribute significantly to the totality of meaning derived from our experience. Ordinarily as adults our private and public communications reflect an easy exchange and blending of all three modes of representation. However, during states of conflict when ideas and feelings are avoided by defensive operations, representational modes may be experienced as separable (Horowitz, 1978; Dosamantes-Alperson, 1983). According to Horowitz (1978) defenses are accomplished by operations at the boundaries of each mode and disavowed ideas or feelings may be unconsciously expressed through those representational modes with which we are less familar or conscious.

Psychologists concerned with human cognitive development agree that the action-based schemata of infancy gradually evolve to include mental images and word concepts (Piaget, 1930; Schilder, 1950; Werner, 1957; Werner and Kaplan, 1964). Singer and Pope (1978) reject a view of cognitive development that would regard the lexical mode as superior to or as supplanting enactive and image modes and argue that all three modes of representing experience are of equal value.

Disavowed Aspects of Experience

The emotional patterns we evolve to deal with important issues in our lives are largely determined by our personal conditioning and acculturation. These patterns in turn influence the kinds of defensive operations we use to avoid being overwhelmed by anxiety (Freud, 1946; Sullivan, 1947; Plutchick, 1954; Tomkins, 1962). Ideas and feelings which we are most likely to ignore, repress, distort or deny are those which are most threatening to the phenomenal self.

By examining the cultural norms that define what is considered nonacceptable, abnormal or deviant in our society, we are able to discover elements of our experence a majority of us fear or dread (Goffman, 1961; Scheff, 1966). These include: not conforming with the work ethic, manifesting altered states of consciousness or primary thought processes, losing emotional control, losing one's body boundaries, being lonely, sustaining intimacy, aging and dying (Karon, 1981; Laing, 1960; Silverman, 1967).

Our culture's preference for the perceptual action mode has led us to regard this mode as the only proper one for adult life and to view states of behavior reflective of the perceptual mode as negatively regressive or as pathological. Additionally, because our culture has tended to prize verbal cognition and communication so highly, it is probably the case that most adults are unfamiliar and disdainful of ways of processing meaning through nonverbal modes (Dosamantes-Alperson, 1980). Fisher (1973) has described how our culture's child-rearing, educational and religious practices have colluded to prevent children from developing more accurate images of their bodies and from trusting and making adaptive use of their bodily feelings. As a society we continue to hold a Cartesian view of the body as a physical machine subordinate to rational thought. We have not yet fully assimilated the fact that "listening to and attending to the wisdom's of one's body is a highly refined and sophisticated act of consciousness" (Geller, 1978, p. 353).

Theoretical Formulations

Experiencing and Self-Actualization

Gendlin (1961) coined the term "experiencing" to refer to the manner in which individuals use their internal, ongoing, bodily-felt flow of experience to gain self-awareness and to communicate about themselves. He regarded experiencing as a quantifiable continuum extending from least to most. At the lowest end of the continuum, one finds individuals who lack contact with their bodily-derived feelings and are blocked in their internal communication (Klein, Mathieu, Gendlin and Kiesler, 1969). At the highest end of the continuum one encounters individuals who can readily tune in to their bodily sensations and feelings, can further differentiate the meaning of this sensed data into words and are able to use it to gain sef-insight (Dosamantes-Alperson, 1981).

In my clinical practice, I have observed the following abilities to be related to a high level of experiencing: (a) ability to perceive one's self as the center of one's experience (internal locus of control), (b) ability to shift readily from active to receptive states of consciousness, (c) ability to maintain a relaxed yet focused type of attention on bodily feelings and spontaneously emerging images,and (d) ability to translate or transform experience from one representational mode to another (e.g., bodily sensations to body movements to images to words). Clients lacking these skills need to be taught them if they are to succeed in exploring themselves in-depth in therapy.

Maslow (9171) referred to individuals who have ready access to their ongoing experiencing and are able to use it as a basis for their actions as self-affirming or self-actualizing. Rogers (1951) found that clients who successfully completed client-centered therapy moved in direction toward increased self-actualization. That is, they became more open to experience, more self-accepting, more inner-directed, more present-time oriented, more responsive to their feelings, and more emotionally responsive to others. An outcome study conducted by the author to test the effectiveness of experiential movement psychotherapy groups yielded similar results (Dosamantes-Alperson and Merrill, 1980). A more detailed description of this study is offered in the Outcome Research section of this chapter. It appears that despite differences found among individual clients relative to the personal content revealed during therapy, that successful therapy clients move in direction towards increased access and use of their experiencing in relation to themselves and others.

Therapeutic Process

Assumptions

It seems to me that to effect a change in how we perceive ourselves and others we need to adopt a receptive attitude toward our experiencing and to engage in a self-explorative process that will let us retrieve, symbolize and process negative or disavowed aspects of ourselves. To derive greater breadth and depth of meaning from our experiencing we need to increase our capacity to differentiate our experience within and across all three experiental modes: enactive, image and lexical.

Definition

Experiential movement psychotherapy seeks to expand individual self awareness and self individualization by exploring the felt-meanings of a client's relationships (actual and internalized) experienced and expressed through any of three experiential modalities. In this approach clients attend to themselves receptively, then they retrieve and work through less conscious aspects of conflicted self and other relationships.

Distinctive Characteristics

Distinctive features which distinguish experiential movement psychotherapy from traditional psychodynamic verbal psychotherapy are: (a) the greater weight given to clients' derivation of personal meaning from their nonverbal experiencing; using movement and imagery as media of experince and emotional expression, (b) the fact that the therapist consistently focuses and maintains the client's attention on his/her bodily-felt experiencing while the client assumes the dual role of experiencer and observer to her/his own experiential process (c) the therapist's acceptance of a somatopsychic view of a client's resistance which encompasses the experience of working through body blocks, blocks in the flow of body movement as well as breaks in the flow of the client's images and verbalized associations, and (d) the attention paid by the therapist to nonverbal aspects of the ongoing therapeutic relationship.

Types of Movement and Imagery Used

In experiential movement psychotherapy two types of authentic body movement (spontaneious, self-initiated and directed) are used: active-interactional movement and receptive-intrapersonal movement (Dosamantes-Alperson, 1979). Active-interactional movement refers to movement which occurs when

270

clients are conscious, quiet and move with their eyes open to relate through movement to actual objects. This type of movement helps clients to perceive emotional patterns they establish with others in their immediate environment. Receptive-intrapersonal movement refers to movement which occurs when clients are in a pre-conscious state and move with their eyes closed to relate to their internal experience. Clients can identify with their internal experence by moving in relation to the images which emerge spontaneously in their awareness. The author has coined the term "kinesthetic images" to refer to the images clients generate from their bodily feelings or sensations and the term "kinetic images" to refer to those images clients generate from their spontaneous body movements or which occur concurrently with their body movements (Dosamantes-Alperson, 1983).

The Process

An experientially-centered movement psychotherapy session proceeds in a zig-zag manner, moving back and forth between the client's preverbal and verbal experience (Dosamantes-Alperson, 1980). In this approach clients learn to transform their bodily-felt experience to images and thoughts. The verbal feedback they obtain when sharing their implicit experiences with others in turn, helps to generate new bodily-felt relationships.

With adults the therapeutic process appears to move through four phases. The first is a preparatory or desensitization phase. During this phase clients learn to attend to their bodily feelings; they learn to adopt simultaneously the role of

271

experiencer and observer to their own
experiential process; they discover what it
feels like to assume a relaxed or receptive
attitude toward their experiencing, and they
learn how to transform bodily feelings to
body movement to images or words.

Methods Employed During Desensitization Phase of Process

Because most clients have problems
shifting automatically to a receptive manner
of attending to themselves, with
differentiating their bodily sensations and
feelings and with moving spontaneously, I
have found it necessary to develop a variety
of methods that would facilitate a client's
contact with his/her own bodily-felt
experiencing. These methods when used are
usually introduced during the preparatory or
desensitization phase of therapy and only
when they appear to be relevant in enhancing
a particular cleint's contact with her/his
own experiential process.

Shifting from Active to Receptive Modes
Through Relaxation. A receptive state of
consciousness is achieved by cleints when
they lie down, close their eyes and relax
(Dosamantes-Alperson, 1980). The closing of
one's eyes has the effect of reducing input
from external stimuli while encouraging wide
or receptive attending to internal stimuli.
Any self-directed relaxation method can be
used to promote this state.

Differentiating Body Feelings Through
Body-Focusing. Many clients suffer from
somatic repression, a condition that
manifests itself as a lack of awareness of
their bodies, bodily reactions and states
(Jourard, 1974). Body-Focusing is a procedure

272

developed to facilitate a person's body-self awareness and feeling reactivity (Dosamantes-Alperson, 1980). While clients are lying down in a relaxed state and their eyes are closed, their attention is drawn by the therapist to their sense of comfort-discomfort. Then they proceed to discriminate polar physical qualities followed by polar emotional qualities of their ongoing bodily experience. With practice this procedure enables clients to "zero in" on the feeling qualities which best describe their emotional state of the moment in any given situation. In therapy this body focusing skill enables clients to tune in readily to "where and what hurts today?"

Undoing Somatic Repression Through Differentiation of Bodily-Felt Experience. The physical manifestation of blocked experience takes the form of a somatic defense. Reich (1949) coined the term "character armor" to describe the individual characteristic postural and movement patterns that result from the inhibition of selective affects. Some of the more prevalent include the avoidance of certain body movements, the loss or alteration of sensations in various parts of their bodies, the experience of body-splits, loss of body boundaries or altered body size, and identification with destructive introjects. Somatic defenses protect clients against the awareness of painful emotional conflict. To the trained observer they reveal directly the nature of the particular client's "problem."

For example, a client who is not always comfortable in social situations, spontaneously imaged herself as a giant during several movement therapy sessions. As she explored moving as her imaged giant, she discovered that she enjoyed the sense of power over others this experience afforded her. In her day to day interactions, this client managed to overcome her fear of closeness and her introversion by behaving in overly expansive and assertive ways. By embodying and moving her "expansiveness" this client was able to experience directly both the adaptive as well as the defensive elements of her relational style.

Transforming Bodily-Felt Experience to Other Modes. When maintaining attention inwardly in a relaxed manner on the single bodily-felt sense which emerges relative to any "problem" that is being worked on at the moment, one begins to differentiate its emotional meaning further and to transform the experence to images and thoughts that bear a relevant emotional connection to the original bodily feeling (Dosamantes-Alperson, 1974). The following clinical excerpt will illustrate how a client was helped to differentiate and to transform her own bodily-felt sensed relationship to a "problem" she was dealing with to other modes of representation (Dosamantes-Alperson, 1983).

Christine experienced her "problem" as a form of tension which she localized in her intestines. As she closed her eyes and began to attend to her experience of tension, she became aware that the tension became more clearly defined as a hard and taut sensation. I encouraged her to conjure up an image from these sensations. The kinesthetic image she generated was that of a large, oozy, blob. This image was immediately transformed by her into an image of a tightly closed fist. She observed that the fist was lodged on one side of her intestines and that she continued to

274

attend to it, the word "mother" spontaneously popped into her head. When she subsequently talked about her nonverbal experience, she alluded to the fact that whenever she related to her mother, her guts would tighten. This happened more frequently when she was angry with her. She also mentioned that she suffered from frequent bouts of constipation which she alleviated with enemas. This nonverbal bodily-felt exploration of her "problem" permitted Christine to perceive the connectoin between her somatic symptoms and her repressed anger toward her mother. It also helped her to perceive the physical toll she had been paying for not finding a more direct means to express her emotions (Dosamantes-Alperson, 1983, p. 337).

During the second phase clients become involved in exploring current conscious aspects of self and other relationships. During the third phase clients become engaged in exploring past, unconscious, primarily nonverbal or preverbal aspects of self and other relationships. During the fourth and final phase, time is spent in acknowledging the impact and conclusion of the special type of relationship established with the therapist.

The Therapeutic Relationship

Experiential therapy involves at least two people in an ongoing relationship (Dosamantes-Alperson, 1976). In the relationship there is one person who is an expert in the detection of felt-meanings, human deception and the promotion of experiential change, and another person who is in pain and is willing to risk engaging in an affective self-explorative process. Because therapists are not simply experts in affective change but are themselves reactive individuals, they need to acknowledge and be conscious of the impact of their reactions on the quality of the ongoing relationship. They do this by tuning empathically to their clients and by learning to use this information to promote shifts in their clients' experiential process. The act of being empathic is a form of intimate understanding that requires that one be able to put oneself accurately into another person's psychological place while simultaneously retaining the awareness that this experience is vicarious (Kern, 1978). It is a preconscious and/or conscious experiential process that makes use of the therapist's fantasies and identifications in attempting to approximate clients' inner states.

Racker (1968) has drawn a distinction between two types of counter-transference identifications therapists have with their clients which I have found most useful in my own work. The first type are concordant identifications. These elicit empathic reactions from the therapist toward the client's expressed thoughts, feelings and behavior. The second type are complementary identifications. These kinds of identifications place the therapist in the emotional position of some projected or unwanted part of the client's self. That is, the client projects some unwanted part of himself/herself on to the therapist; the therapist then experiences these feelings and impulses toward the client.

Experiential movement psychotherapists function as creative artists who swing reciprocally between their intuition and their intellect. They trust the working of the preconscious and allow themselves to be influenced by primary thought processes to derive therapeutic hunches and insights. However, they also use their intellect to check intuitive hunches for fit and to perceive patterns and a direction in the unfolding therapeutic process.

Their behavior reflects the interplay of these two functions in action. On the other hand, they attend receptively to the felt-meanings revealed by their clients and to the emotional tenor of the evolving therapeutic relationship. On the other hand, they use these perceptions to guide their interventions and to gauge the progress of the therapeutic process; providing the degree of structure clients might need to feel safe while forwarding their experiential process. Their therapeutic strategies take into consideration the developmental histories, established emotional patterns, defenses and strengths of their clients.

Kinesthetic Empathy. Winnicott (1958) and Laing (1968) have stressed the need for patients to develop a "true self" by avoiding an "impingement" upon them during preverbal stages of therapeutic regression. Winnicott (1958) described the optimal attitude of the therapist under these conditions as a "holding" object, a function akin to basic mothering for individuals for whom "good enough mothering" was lacking. At such moments, a silent regression takes place to what amounts a primitive form of dependency on the therapist experienced as a "holding mother." At such times, the therapist's intuitive, empathic understanding presence may be sufficient in contrast to the disturbing, intrusively expierenced effects of verbal communication.

As an experiential movement psychotherapist I make sense of my clients' kinesthetic responses by recreating their movements in my own body in the abbreviated and coded form of incipient body movements. This kinesthetic empathy enables me to sense and respond to a client's emotional state of the moment (Dosamantes-Alperson, 1980).

The following case study will describe in fuller detail a client's process as she worked through the various phases of experiential movement psychotherapy, initially within the context of a group and subsequently in individual private sessions.

Case Study

Marion is an attractive brunette in her early forties. She is college educated and married. Anticipating the graduation of her youngest of two daughters from high school, she decided to return to school to pursue a career as a school psychologist.

She spent the first phase of therapy as a "curious" but anonymous participant in a beginning experiential movement psychotherapy group offered at the university she attended. None of the participants in this group had previous dance therapy or dance training. The group met for two-hour long sessions twice weekly for ten weeks.

The group moved through a series of semi-structured movement experiences that were intended to familiarize participants with desensitization phase level nonverbal

experiences (e.g., group participants learned
to differentiate body parts, bodily
sensations and feelings, to move
spontaneously in self-directed ways alone or
with others and to transform their experience
across all three experiential modes). Time
was left in each session so that those who
wished could verbally share their private
nonverbal experience.

Because for the most part, Marion kept
her nonverbal experiencing within the group
private (she only commented on her experience
twice), whatever understanding I was able to
gain about her psychodynamics, came primarily
from her movement and nonverbal behavior
within the group:

> Marion preferred active to
> receptive movement. She found it
> extremely difficult to relax. Her
> individual active movement style could
> be characterized as heavy, bound, slow,
> abrupt and possessing a premeditated and
> predictable quality. She lacked
> lightness and spontaneity.

> When standing or moving in an
> upright position, she thrusted her chest
> forward but kept her arms and hands
> close to her body. Most of the time she
> kept her hands inside her pants'
> pockets. She never spontaneously reached
> out to others. When sitting down, she
> folded her legs in front of her in a
> yoga-like position, bent her torso
> inward toward her solar plexus and
> covered her entire face and upper torso
> with her long straight hair.

> While she would readily follow
> movement cues provided by the therapist
> which were compatible with her

individual and interactional movement style preferences, she abstained from trying out those which were unfamiliar or dissimilar to her own.

She preferred to move alone. When moving with another person, she tended to initiate the relationship as well as the movement interactions. She generally chose an introverted and passive middle-aged woman as a partner. When she moved as part of the group she moved cautiously preferring to remain at the periphery of the room and to keep large distances from others. Within the larger context of the group, she was a follower rather than an initiator of group interactions.

Marion shared her movement experience explicitly only twice. The first time was when she was able to relax fully and to let go of tension throughout her entire body. She expressed surprise at finding the experience "pleasurable" and "soothing." Clinically this was a significant experience for Marion found that she was able to sense her usual bound and controlled state at a bodily-felt level. Consequently, she learned to release it under her direction and she was able to experience the pleasurable effect that ensued.

The second experience Marion shared explicitly had to with receptively exploring her personal space through a self-generated kinetic image. She was puzzled that she had chosen to stay within the confines of her personal space boundaries rather than to venture out to face the outside world. Apparently, this experience was incongruous with her own self-image as an intrepid almost adventuresome person who would impulsively try anything. This self-disconfirming incongruous experience helped to put Marion in touch with her actual relational style and with her fear and reticence of venturing out beyond the boundaries of her familiar psychological personal space.

A month after the group ended Marion contacted me for individual movement psychotherapy sessions. I was surprised by her request since in the group she had impressed me as one of the more reticent and withholding members. We agreed to meet for one hour a week on an ongoing basis.

The second phase of Marion's therapy lasted approximately eight months. During this phase Marion moved to explore significant othrs' expectations of her, to discover her competence as a special school counselor, to extend her sphere of influence beyond the boundaries of her home, and to become more assertive in relations with members of her immediate family, demanding more for herself and making her needs explicit and clear to them.

This phase began with her talking and actively moving the roles she thought others expected her to fulfill. According to her, her mother wanted her to be "the perfect and obedient adolescent" while her husband expected her to be a "good homemaker" who made his life at home more comfortable. Her two daughters hoped she would remain a "good mother" and not become an autonomous adult with needs of her own.

Marion explored the limitations these roles imposed on her as well as the safety and security they provided for her. She became aware that by assuming these roles they had indeed become part of her identity. However, now that she was conscious of their

281

effect on her, she also had the option to try out new ways of being she felt to be more congruent with her own needs.

She then began to look for ways to assert her autonomy outside of the home. She got a job working as a special school counselor at a school for emotionally disturbed children. In this setting she received much appreciation and recognition for being one of the institution's most effective counselors. She also developed her own set of friends and spent a great deal of time away from home pursuing her own interests and continuing her education.

At home Marion made it clear that she wanted each family member to contribute something to the upkeep of the household. Initially they resisted her new found assertiveness, but eventually they acknowledged that she had changed for the better. The feedback they gave her was that she had become "more complex and interesting" and they appreciated her being able "to stand her own ground."

Toward the end of this phase, Marion requested that we move together. As we did, I became aware that she maintained great distances from me and that she found it extremely difficult to initiate and sustain contact with me. At these times Marion would stretch her arms out towards me only to retreat and close up abruptly as soon as I responded to her gesture through movement. I was aware that it was difficult for her to maintain a sense of her own integrity and independence while simultaneously letting herself become dependent on me. I let her know I understood "how hard it must be to be a grown up while needing to be held." Soon she asked that we stop moving altogether. At

this point she decided to terminate therapy
though I pointed out that she seemed to be
running away from important unfinished
business between us. While she agreed with
this assessment, she felt compelled "to take
a breather" and to stop therapy for the time
being.

Two months later Marion called me to say
that she wished to resume her individual
movement therapy sessions. She commented that
while she was "petrified about treading into
unknown territory," she had missed our
relationship and had been deeply depressed
over the loss of her contact with me. By
contrast to the previous phase which dealt
with problematic but conscious aspects of her
immediate relationships, the third phase was
characterized by a series of regressive
periods that led her to explore receptively
nonverbal and preverbal aspects of her
internalized relationship with her mother.

During the first session of this phase,
Marion let me know that while she had missed
me she had also been angry with me for not
insisting that she stay in therapy. I
reminded her that it was she who had made the
decision to leave. I also let her know that I
would not be destroyed by her anger nor would
I deprive her of the right to decide for
herself whether or not to continue her
therapy.

The next session proved to be
particularly significant for it shifted the
focus of therapy to a less conscious
preverbal exploration of her maternal
relationship. The session was entirely
nonverbal. She began by moving receptively at
a distance from me. There she assumed her
usual curled-in sitting down position with
her hair covering her upper torso and her

face. After a while she laid flat on her stomach and began to roll herself nearer to me. As she made contact with my feet, she curled up next to me in a fetal-like position. I shifted my sitting position to a complementary reclining one. With our bodies barely touching, we spent the remainder of the session breathing softly and synchronously together. As we breathed I had an image that we were both merged and gliding blissfully together in space. Clinically this was an important session for Marion for it allowed her to merge with me and to confront her fear of maternal engulfment and obliteration.

In the next session Marion went on to describe her mother as a controlling, perfectionist woman who could not tolerate strong emotions in herself or others. She described her father as a passive man who had allowed her mother to "rule the roost." According to her, he was equally uncomfortable with any display of emotions and preferred to intellectualize his relationships.

To gain her mother's approval as a child Marion had learned to behave as the perfect model child her mother wished for--a child who excelled in school, a child who never cried, never demanded any affection from her, never got angry with her nor challenged her authority. Marion claimed to have "hidden" what she really felt "deep inside" of her. She went on to describe herself as an adult as a strong, self-sufficient, perfectionist person who hated to be wrong about anything because it made her feel stupid and vulnerable to fantasied recriminations from others. While the realization that as an adult she had internalized many of the attributes she "detested" in her mother which deeply upset and saddened Marion, it also gave her the impetus to continue to explore unrealized facets of herself.

During subsequent sessions she began to explore aspects of herself her mother had not approved of which she herself had either repressed or denied--her rage, her experience of deprivation, her loneliness, her vulnreability with its tenderness and softness, her fear that behind the "pretend facade" she presented to others there would be "no inner-core" and that she would encounter nothing but an "empty void"; her need as well as her fear for nurturance and support.

I believe that the supportive but non-possessive environment I was able to provide Marion enabled her to regress and to re-experience negative aspects of her maternal relationship she had internalized. Following the recognition and acceptance of these negative attributes within herself, Marion was able to recover and to reintegrate significant dissociated, split or denied aspects of herself (i.e., she was able to integrate the "compliant good-girl facade" she presented to the world at large which she experienced as "false" with those dissociated, repressed or denied aspects of herself she experienced as more "authentic" but early had learned to "hide" from her mother.)

At this writing Marion was moving toward the end of the third phase of therapy.

Outcome Research

A two-year study which sought to evaluate the effectiveness of experiential

movement psychotherapy in producing
personality changes was carried out by the
author (Dosamantes-Alperson and Merrill,
1980). In this study pre/post measures
obtained from two experimental experiential
movement psychotherapy groups (composed of
adult volunteers without dance training) were
compared with pre/post measures obtained from
two control groups (a ballet class and a
waiting-list control group drawn from the
same population as the experimental groups).
The results demonstrated significant changes
due to experiential movement psychotherapy
with respect to six measures of degree of
self-actualization (inner-directedness,
existentiality, feeling reactivity,
spontaneity, self-acceptance and capacity for
intimate contact) as well as with respect to
a measure of body-self acceptance.

Pre/post individual expressive movement
ratings made on one of the experimental
groups also indicated significant changes in
the amount of space covered while moving, in
use of the whole body while moving, and in
the greater use of expansive and lighter
movement qualities.

Bibliography

Blanck, G. and Blanck, R. Ego Psychology II:
    Psychoanalytic Developmental Psychology.
    New York: Columbia University Press,
    1979.

Bruner, J. S. "The Course of Cognitive
    Psychology." American Psychologist,
    1964, 19, 1-15.

Combs, A. W., Richards, A. C. and Richards, F. Perceptual Psychology: A Humanistic Approach to the Study of Persons. New York: Harper and Row, 1976.

Deikman, A. J. "Bimodal Consciousness and the Mystic Experience." In R. E. Ornstein (Ed.) Symposium on Consciousness. New York: Viking Press, 1976.

Dosamantes-Alperson, E. "Carrying Experiencing Forward Through Authentic Body Movement." Psychotherapy: Theory, Research and Practice, 1974, 11, 211-214.

_____. "Experiential Movement Psychotherapy." Art Psychotherapy, 1976, 3, 20-31.

_____. "The Intrapsychic and the Interpersonal in Movement Psychotherapy." American Journal of Dance Therapy, 1979, 3, 20-31.

_____. "Contacting Bodily-felt Experiencing in Psychotherapy." In J. E. Shorr, G. E. Sobel, P. Robbin and J. Connella (Eds.). Imagery: Its Many Dimensions and Applications. New York: Plenum Press, 1980.

_____. "Experiencing in Movement Psychotherapy." American Journal of Dance Therapy, 1981, 4, 33-44.

_____. "Working With Internalized Relationships Through a Kinesthetic and Kinetic Imagery Process." Imagination, Cognition and Personality, 1983, 2 (4), 333-343.

_____ and Merrill, N. "Growth Effects of
Experiential Movement Psychotherapy."
Psychotherapy: Theory, Research and
Practice, 1980, 17, 63-68.

Erikson, E. Childhood and Society. New York:
W. W. Norton, 1950.

Fairbairn, W. R. D. An Object-Relations
Theory of Personality. New York: Basic
Books, 1954.

Field, J. A life of One's Own. London: Chatto
and Windus, 1952.

Fisher, S. Body Consciousness. New Jersey:
Prentice-Hall, 1973.

Freud, A. The Ego and the Mechanisms of
Defense. New York: International
Universities Press, 1946.

Freud, S. "A Note on the Unconscious in
Psycho-analysis." In J. Riviere Sigmund
Freud Collected Papers. New York: Basic
Books, 1959.

Geller, J. D. "Body, Expressive Movement and
Physical Contact in Psychotherapy." In
J. L. Singer and K. S. Pope (Eds.) The
Power of Human Imagination. New York:
Plenum Press, 1978.

Gendlin, E. T. "Experiencing: A Variable in
the Process of Therapeutic Change."
American Journal of Psychotherapy, 1961,
15, 233-245.

Goffman, E. Asylums. New York: Doubleday-
Anchor, 1961.

288

Horowitz, M. J. "Mode of Representation of Thought." Journal of the American Psychoanalytic Association, 1972, 20, 793-819.

____. "Controls of Visual Imagery and Therapist Intervention." In J. L. Singer and K. S. Pope (Eds.) The Power of Human Imagination. New York: Plenum Press, 1978.

Jacobson, E. The Self and the Object World. New York: International Universities Press, 1954.

Jourard, S. M. Healthy Personality. New York: Macmillan, 1974.

Karon, B. P. and VandeBos, G. R. Psychotherapy of Schizophrenia. New York: Jason Aronson, 1981.

Kern, J. W. "Countertransference and Spontaneous Screens: An Analyst Studies His Own Visual Images." Journal of American Psychoanalytic Association, 1978, 26, 21-47.

Kestenberg, J. S. Children and Parents: Psychoanalytic Studies in Development. New York: Jason Aronson, 1975.

Klein, M. S. The Psycho-Analysis of Children. New York: W. W. Norton, 1932.

Klein, M., Mathieu, L. P., Gendlin, E. T. and Kiesler, D. J. The Experiencing Scale: A Research and Training Manual (Vols. 1 and 2). Madison, Wisconsin: Wisconsin Psychiatric Institute, 1969.

Laing, R. D. The Divided Self: A Study of Sanity and Madness. London: Tavistock Press, 1968.

Mahler, M. S. On Human Symbiosis and the Vicissitudes of Individuation. New York: International Universities Press, 1968.

_____, Pine, F. and Bergman, A. The Psychological Birth of the Human Infant. New York: Basic Books, 1975.

Maslow, A. H. The Farther Reaches of Human Nature. New York: Viking Press, 1971.

Merton, R. K. "The Self-fulfilling Prophecy." Antioch Review, 1948, 8, 193-210.

Ornstein, R. E. The Psychology of Consciousness. New York: Viking Press, 1972.

Piaget, J. The Child's Perception of Physical Causality. New York: Harcourt, 1930.

Plutchick, R. "The Role of Muscular Tension in Maladjustment." Journal of General Psychology, 1954, 50, 45-62.

Racker, H. Transference and Counter-transference. New York: International Universities Press, 1968.

Reich, W. Character Analysis. New York: Farrar, Straus and Giroux, 1949.

Rogers, C. R. Client-Centered Therapy. Boston: Houghton and Mifflin, 1951.

Scheff, T. J. Being Mentally Ill. Chicago: Aldine Publishing, 1966.

Schilder, P. The Image and Appearance of the
    Human Body. New York: International
    Universities Press, 1950.

Silverman, J. "Shamans and Acute
    Schizophrenia." American Anthropologist,
    1967, 69, 21-31.

Singer, J. L. and Pope, K. S. "The Use of
    Imagery and Fantasy Techniques in
    Psychotherapy." In J. L. Singer and K.
    S. Pope (Eds.) The Power of Human
    Imagination. New York: Plenum Press,
    1978.

Sullivan, H. S. Conceptions of Modern
    Psychiatry. Washington, D.C.: William
    Alanson White Psychiatric Foundations,
    1947.

Tomkins, S. Affect, Imagery and
    Consciousness, Vol. I. New York:
    Springer, 1962.

Werner, H. Comparative Psychology and Mental
    Development. New York: International
    Universities Press, 1957.

Werner, H. and Kaplan, B. Symbol Formation:
    An Organismic Developmental Approach to
    Language and the Expression of Thought.
    New York: John Wiley and Sons, 1964.

Winnicott, D. W. "Ego Distortion in Terms of
    True and False Self." In The
    Maturational Process and the
    Facilitating Environment. New York:
    International Universities Press, 1958.

The Invisible Dance: The Embodied Bipersonal Field

The Somatic Unconscious and Its Relation to the Embodied Feminine in Dance-Movement Therapy Process*

Penny Lewis Bernstein, Ph.D., ADTR

Matriarchal Consciousness

Before the logos ordering the patriarchal solar consciousness took over Western civilization, the Great Goddess was the source of society's values and worship (Campbell, 1973; Harding, 1971; Hall, 1980; Neumann, 1973; Graves, 1979; Pomeroy, 1975; Singer, 1973). As ancient as the venus figurines of 30,000 B.C., the female has been invoked and revered as the personification of mystery, healing and at-oneness with the laws of nature. Hillman (1971) notes that a relation to the feminine principle "has been an essential ingredient for health and wholeness" in both eastern and western traditions (from Krishna, p. 158). The feminine perspective is receptive and

---

*This chapter was first presented at the 1981 American Dance Therapy Assocation Conference in Madison, Wisc., under the title of "Moon Goddess, Medium, and Earth Mother: A Phenomenological Study of the Guiding Feminine Archetypes of the Dance-Movement Therapist."

understands the wisdom which lives in the intuitive. Eric Neumann (1973) writes, "it is wisdom that is bound and stays to the earth, to organic growth and to ancestral experience. It is the wisdom of the unconscious, of the instincts, of life and of relationship," (pp. 56-57). Matriarchal consciousness understands and values the cyclic quality of nature and within it the need for destruction to fertilize the rebirthing of all life.

This eternal process is known not solely through cogitation as with patriarchal wisdom, but through body experience as well. Woman knows her own physical connection to the cyclic through her lunar influenced menstrual cycles and through the fertilizing, gestating, birthing, and nurturing of all humankind. Unlike the male-god view, the goddess does not rule the world, she embodies it (Starhawk, 1979). Thus her orientation is to organic growth rather than logical or mechanical causation (Neumann, 1973, p. 54). "Processes of growth are processes of transformation and subject to the Self. Matriarchal consciousness mirrors these processes and in its specific way accompanies and supports them" (Neumann, 1973, p. 52).

In discussing modern woman's relation to this consciousness, Pomeroy (1975) writes, "There is as it were a certain fundamental 'synchronicity' in her relation to her feminine psyche. And it is this synchronisticity which is the presence of spirit in her archaic feminine world, a spirit manifesting itself not solely as light but in wind symbols and rhythmic movement, as in the waves in which wind and water meet, and as a sort of imminent luminosity, a liquid phosphorescence, a heater's glowing, as of the sea on a summer's night, which represents a projected reflection of her insight into the darkness of her prima materia" (p. 37).

This consciousness is not, of course, confined to women alone. Men who have integrated the feminine or anima within them are influenced by these perspectual horizons and experiences. Hillman (1971) writes, "Feminine power cannot be made to serve the masculine principle. The goddess is not activated to serve man, but the feminine force or anima must have its own channel of activity, and man if only an instrument through which this force manifests itself" (from Krishna, p. 157).

But for the most part our culture has continued to reinforce patriarchal principles spiritually, culturally, politically, and psychologically, both in men and women (Harding, 1971; Hall, 1980; Campbell, 1973; Neumann, 1973). Masculine logos has been actively attempting to empirically analyze all of existence. Anything that cannot fit within the confines of scientific methodology is devalued and often purported not to exist. The myopic mechanistic Western logic system is unable to value mystery and that which cannot be reduced and placed under a microscope. Luke (1980) writes, "True mysteries need to be kept silent, so that they may transform us from within. Without mystery, all of our fine intellecutal understanding and its great value turns to dust" (p. 22).

Even the field of psychotherapy which is designed to "integrate and facilitate an individual's experience of wholeness" is caught in this unipolar malaise. Jungian analyst Anita Greene (1980) writes, "one wonders whether the largely patriarchal background of the analytic and psychiatric establishment may not be lacking in the differentiated relationship to anima, the feminine, and body" (p. 93).

What is being explored here is an avenue in which our culture may move closer toward the tao of the polarities of the matriarchal and patriarchal archetypes so that an integrating continuum may exist between the various elements which reflect these views. (Figure 1 represents a compilation of some of the typical perspectives of these two points of view.)

Dance-Movement Therapy and the Matriarchal

For those familiar with the fundamental principles of dance-movement therapy, certain concepts and phrases may stand out in the above listing. The polarities of experience and analytic perspective; spatial and verbal; sensuous, physical and intellectual; creating and generalizing--maintaining; as well as the value in the intuitive, natural timing, and in the unconscious as a source of information and wisdom all have direct relationship to the basic concepts and orientations of dance-movement therapy. Clearly, dance therapy readily adheres to matriarchal or feminine principles as well as the patriarchal. The fact that this is a female dominated profession will not be explored here, although I doubt that anyone could argue that the abundance of women therapists has not influenced the value and adherence to the feminine perspective. Rather, this chapter attempts to explore how the female archetypal constellates itself and facilitates the work of the dance-movement therapist.

Matriarchal Archetypal View	Patriarchal Archetypal View
intuition	reason
experience	analytic perspective
synchronistic, simultaneous	causal, sequential
spatial	verbal
earth	air
water	fire
receptive	active
tacit	explicit
eternity, timeless	time oriented
sensuous, physical	intellectual
night	day
protection	competition
nourish	possess
communal property	individual property
fertilizing spirit	sterile dryness
creative, inspirational	capacity to generalize/ discriminate
wisdom which lies in instinct	wisdom which lies in consciousness
right hemisphere	left hemisphere
eros	logos
cyclic	linear
darkness holds unconscious secret to life	darkness holds ignorance, consciousness holds answers
creating--destroying	maintaining-- unchanging
yin	yang
mystery, vision	clarity
qualitative	quantitative
power of nature	authority of society
heroine as having mythic embodiment in herself	hero as needing to "gain" his powers

Figure 1. Matriarchal and Patriarchal Perspectives. (Compiled from Campbell, 1973, Neumann, 1973; Whitmont, 1980, Bernstein, 1981)

299

Research

Purpose of This Study

The purpose of this research is to reveal the existence of and explicate the dance-movement therapist's experience of the intuitive in which the source is felt to be beyond that of the therapist's own personal/interprsonal ken. The study is interested in revealing the specific somatic unconscious processes along with the therapist's associations to them. The relationship of these phenomena to the experience of feminine archetypes within the collective unconscious is discussed with specific focus on numinous experiences within the constellation of the archetypes of Moon Goddess, medium, and Earth Mother.

Being part of a patriarchal culture which focuses on empiricism and quantitative programming as methods of validation does not leave much room for the exploration of the meaning of these phenomena. Yet the need for this type of study remains. Experiences of knowing from a non causal origin need to come out from the shadow position within the continuum of the sources of wisdom and understanding. Conscious left hemisphere intellectual explicit rationality needs to be balanced with the right hemisphere intuitive which draws from body felt experience, creativity, instinct and a synchronistically based timeless natural source.

From the phenomenological analysis of the five theories presented in this book, it is clear that the fundamental principles of dance-movement therapy which are implicit in all approaches adhere to and reinforce an androgenous perspective which respects the basic matriarchal right brain point of view. The dance-movement therapist literally and figuratively embodies this orientation to life and growth. The facilitators of this field may thus be the new constellators of this form of consciousness thereby assisting individuals and, in a larger perspective, the culture, toward an androgynous rebalancing.

In order to research this phenomena, a qualitative depth focus on the experience of the matriarchal consciousness within the dance therapist's work is needed. In this manner, the impact and value of a way of being-in-the-world can be explored in relation to the interpersonal horizon of therapist and client/patient. Thus a phenomenological method of research has been selected--as it encourages and allows for the clarification of experience in a way that facilitates appreciation of the essence of meaning (Bernstein, 1979). The emphasis is placed on the phenomenon as it reveals itself to the subject who is experiencing it (Giorgi, 1971).

Review of Literature

Research, too, has been infused with a patriarchal value system. Unless the study employed a quantitative empirical experimental design, very little weight and merit is given to it. A patriarchal perspective is incompatible with the intensive qualitative scrutiny of data which is required for this study. The comparative analysis of the implicit theory and basic body of knowledge of dance-movement therapy in volume one along with the reduction of an individual's experience of a puberty rite of passage in dance therapy (1981) reflects the only employment of this methodology in the field. Neither studies address themselves to the experience in question.

Phenomena of this nature can be found in case studies of Jungian dance therapists such as Whitehouse (1980), Smallwood (1978), Bernstein (1980), and Fay (1977). Bartenieff (1980) in her _Body Movement Coping with the Environment_ quotes Rudolf Laban in his discussion of the movement choirs. "The dancer in the movement choir expresses himself, but more enhanced and nearer to an archetypal ideal" (p. 139). But none have specifically focused upon nor researched this archetypal connection and experience in the work of movement therapist.

Phenomena of this nature have been left to parapsychologists such as Krippner (1968), Tart (1975), and Ornstein (1972) and to more spiritual quasi-religious communities.

Method, Population and Design

The present study analyzed transcribed interviews and written statements made by dance therapists in response to the following questions:

1. Have you ever had an experience of the intuitive during a dance therapy session in which you experienced somatic sensations and/or movement from a source which was beyond your personal/interpersonal ken?

2. If you have had such an experience(s), would you describe it paying specific attention to your somatic process, your associations to it, and the impact it had on the movement therapy process?

Dance therapists were selected based on their years of experience in the field, the variety of training and theoretical approaches they represented, the various populations with whom they worked, and their proportionate geographic distribution. Psychoanalytic, ego psychology, existential, family systems theory, Jungian, Gestalt, transpersonal, and psychodynamic frames of reference are represented along with approaches influenced by training from Chace, Schoop, Bartenieff, Evan, and Whitehouse. Populations of client/patients include children, with autism, psychosis, and other emotional disturbances as well as those with institutionalizable psychosis and depressive disroders; outpatients as well as neurotic and character disordered clients found in private practice; and geriatric individuals with organic and functional impairments. All of these dance therapists are registered and have trained graduate dance therapy students. Their orientations include individuals, groups, couples, and families.

Assumptions

Certain assumptions are made which represent the bias of the interviewer. The following statements are adapted from a compendium of Psi beliefs and theories (Dean, 1979, p. 15). The parenthetic material represent Jungian analytic concepts. "Psychogeny recapitulates cosmogeny, i.e. the developing mind includes an innate awareness of the origin and meaning of the universe" (existence of a priori collective unconscious).

The ultraconscious state (experience of the archetypal) bridges the evolutionary gap

and produces cosmis awareness
(synchronicity).

"Psi power (or the synchronistic
experience of the numinously intuitive) is
latent in all, and an experiential reality to
many."

Results

Fundamental Unsituated Structure

A dance-movement therapist's bodily felt
experience with the numinously intuitive
commences with a preparatory phase of
internal somatic changes in which breathing
is altered. Frequently a readiness and a
sense of waiting is precipitated by a sense
of visceral emptying producing a vessel-like
receptivity. Concomitantly ego based needs
and individuality is lessened and an
awareness and sensitivity to the surroundings
is heightened.

During the middle phase an experience of
energy originating from outside the body
surges into and often through the individual.
A feeling of connection to an essential
powerful core results.

In the final phase of the potential for
intervention, the essential energy core
guides the subject in a compelling manner
toward the experience of knowing during the
movement therapy session.

Discussion of Fundamental
Unsituated Structure

The essential invariant structures of
each of the protocols are strikingly similar
in many respects. All therapists describe the
phenomenon of an experience of the
synchronistically intuitive as a bodily felt
one. Three main phases of the experience
reveal themselves. There is an initial
preparation phase in which the dance
therapistts sensed internal somatic changes
and a concomitant lessening of a sense of
personal ego-self awareness. Breathing
changes occurred typically resulting in a
quieting, sustained more refined flow of
breath. The subjects describe a sense of
internal receptivity with the majority
experiencing their internal viscera as
"becoming a liquid," "invisible" emptiness to
produce a "pleasant void," a "vessel"-like
container.

A self focus dissolves. Idiosyncratic
ego directed voluntary movement is stilled. A
heightened awareness and sensitivity
develops. One therapist describes a liquid-
like awareness of the total environment;
another of being able to see 360 at once;
another describes a time/space suspension;
and another a feeling of shifting into a more
primitive perceptual sense.

In the middle phase all the dance-
movement therapists experience a rush of
energy entering their body. The energy, which
has been described as brightness, light
energy, creative energy, and shock-like,
typically entered the head and flowed through
the body. The need to maintain grounding is
figural for some of the subjects. In
contrast, one therapist describes the energy
as entering the vaginal canal. It centers, as

305

it does in others, in the pelvic area. Most, if not all therapists experience a feeling of power, the origin of which is other than the individual. Some feel possessed; others feel an essential core/Self/soul connection.

The final phase produces a deep "absolutely right" knowing of the client or group in the moment and results in the potential for intervention. Therapists stated that something came into consciousness which "guided," "compeled," "triggered" or "pulled" them to knowing and possible response. With a trust in the rightness of this experience, comes an allowing of this phenomenon to impact the therapists' sessions.

All the subjects feel that the source of this energy and resultant sense of knowing is other than self and client or group. Most assert that it comes from a universal transcendant source although many, perhaps because of their conceptual orientations, are somewhat uncomfortable hearing themselves reflect in this manner. It is described as a primordial universal life force which taps into a creative energy resource, a light which connects to other sources of knowing, and a transcendant place where opposites meet and are united. One therapist describes an internal landscape created by cosmic life force. Another therapist facilitating a group feels herself to be as a witch midwife guiding an ancient mysterious communal ritual.

Relationship to Moon Goddess, Medium, and Earth Mother as Guiding Archetypes

Earth Mother

Matriarchal consciousness was first personified and deified through the Mother

Goddess or Earth Mother. She was a dominant in cults of the Bronze Age and was present in Mesopotamia as Namma and Ishtar, then in classical Greece as Ge, Rhea, Hera, Cybele, and Demeter, in Rome as Ceres and Tellus and as Au Set and Isis she was the national dividity of Egypt beginning circa 2500 B.C.. Altars to Isis continued to be found in 2nd century A.D. Italy. She is Spider Woman of the Pueblo, and Changing Woman of the Navajo.

The Earth Woman is the goddess of fertility, of union and of the possibility of birth. She is loving mother, the healer of the sick, the resurrector of the dead toward the experience of rebirth (Pomeroy, 1975). Apuleius' The Golden Ass or Metamorporphoses is a classic example of her assistance in a hero's individuation process (Hillman from Krishna, 1971, p. 152). She is the Hindu Shakti "supreme mistress of the body" representing active creative energy (Arguelles, 1977), the pwerful dynamic primal energy force of the universe (Stone, 1979).

> "She unwinds herself through the
>   Chakras
> through the lotuses of the body
> as she creates her cosmic serpent
>   spiral
> through the lotus Chakras of the
>   universe" (Stone, 1979, p. 16).

Hall (1980) writes regarding Ishtar, "In women she is asking for reverence, that we see ourselves with dry eye capable of the turn from tenderness to the mad devouring of our own creations. She asks us to learn the dance 'in which the dances contradict the waste and easy gesture'--to know our own 'true hips'--of what swaying and standing firm our bodies are capable" (p. 16).

It is in the Eleusinian Mystery rites of Demeter and Kore-Persephone that a highly specific connection to the dance therapists' experience of the numinously intuitive reveals itself. In the myth Kore, Demeter's daughter is abducted by Dis, god of darkness, raped and taken to the underworld. Without Persephone, who represents her mother's creativity and fecundity, the earth lies fallow. The instinctual unconscious has captured and imprisoned this aspect of woman's psychology. Demeter is overwhelmed with feelings of grief and ire. Her youthful innocence has been taken from her. She finally reaches the "sacred maiden well" to "tap buried information" from the depths of the collective unconscious. This inward journey eventually draws her into the deeper understanding of the necessity for destruction, for autumn and winter, in order for the fertility of spring and summer to occur (Hall, Harding).

The well at Eleusius can still be seen, as can the trodden circle that the dancers left that performed the yearly mystery rite in honor of Demeter and the rhythm of death and birth (Hall, 1980, p. 63).

Numerous heroic myths from various cultures recount a return to a well, cave, or other symbolic wombs as a requirement for initiation to greater knowing and integration (Eliade, 1958). Direct relationship to the white goddess, however, results not in worshipping her, but rather "embodying her." It would appear that not only the goddess, but her mythic quest as well, is somatically personified. Before the actual experience of creative energy force flowing into the bodies of some subjects of this study, a specific somatic experience of a "visceral void" surrounded by an outer "shell" or "vessel"

was described. Mother Isis was often
worshipped and represented as a vase of
water. Harding (1963) writes, "The vessel
becomes the chalice containing the spiritual
draught. The mother, originally the giver of
physical life, is now the life-giver on the
spiritual plane. This transition was already
hinted at in the symbolism of the Celtic
cauldron (of Cerridwen) which was the
forerunner of the Holy Grail" (p. 177). In
these instances it was as if the therapist's
body was transformed into a womblike well to
await the energy from the universal pool of
knowing. These subjects as well as other
therapists then experience a sense of giving
birth to a creative movement improvisation or
a gestalted holographic experience of the
client/patient and their psychosomatic
dynamics.

It is the qualities of the Earth Mother
archetype which provide therapists and thus
their clients with the view of the
therapeutic process as an ongoing experience
of the death and rebirth cycle through the
awareness and working through of conflict
toward greater integration.

The powerful surging often described as
universal energy that all subjects related is
experienced as flowing into and frequently
through the body. Shakti as the
personification of body felt creative goddess
energy is clearly consonant with this
phenomenon. Krishna describes Prana-Shakti as
the "medium by which the cosmic intelligence
conducts the unimaginably vast activity of
this world" (p. 108). Analytically, Shakti
represents the totality of the Objective
Psyche or Self. The aim of archetypal
manifestation of the Kundalini meditation is
enlightenment through the somatic arousal of
Shakti. During this process Krishna (1971)

describes similar body sensations and alterations to those of the subjects. Hillman (1971) comments on Krishna's experience, "Alteration of consciousness does not leave the body out." Bodily changes occur "as necessary preparation for enlarged consciousness." Here again the body is viewed as a "vessel" (p. 97) to be filled.

Medium Priestess

The medium represents the magical, spiritual, psychic perspective of feminine consciousness. She is personified as the Greek Sibyl, the Celtic Cerridwen, and the wise old women of folk tales and myths. As the oracle of Apollo at Delphi, she was the supreme link between the gods and mortals. She was considered a healer, a weaver and translater of dreams and visions. The medial woman, Hall writes, is "in touch with the essential life-sustaining stratum of experience and knows that dance and song are as necessary for survival as food preparation" (p. 162). She goes on to say that the work of this woman is "transformation: making something out of nothing; giving form to formless energy" (p. 169).

She does this by invoking the inner spirit energy through a form of possession. The vessel-like phenomena is also reflected within this medial experience as well. Toni Wolff (1973) is quoted as saying, "The mediumistic type is rather like a passive vessel for contents which lie outside it, and which are either simply lived or else are being formed. In this sense she is immensely valuable in giving shape to what is still invisible" (de Castillejo, 1973, p. 67).

Castillejo writes, "She is permeated by the unconscious of another person and makes it visible by living it. She may pick up what is going on beneath the surface of the group" (p. 67) and give it shape.

The capacity to invoke energy of an intuitive quality is a phenomenon that all subjects have in common. The experiencing of the lessening of personal idiosyncratic ego in order for a receptive and in some instances vessel-like somato-psychic experience is another felt sense that the therapists described.

A heightened awareness of the client/patients and the therapeutic environment providing a capacity to give "form to the formless" is active in all the subjects' process of intervention. The form might manifest itself via thematic movement improvisations or an internal rich understanding of the client.

Finally, a possession-like transformational experience was specifically described by a few of the subjects. One related, "I felt a tremendous surge of powerful enregy. It was if I could have been possessed." While another felt herself to be in a "trance state." Still another describes being "empowered." She relates, "By simultaneously receiving and becoming the changes, I am constantly transforming myself."

Moon Goddess

The Moon Goddess is also associated with healing, she is the midwife to those giving birth, protectorate of the newborn, a teacher of women, a sister to men, a huntress, a

311

woman of the wildnerness and a leader of the
dance (Hall, Harding). As the triple goddess,
Artemis, Diana and other moon deities, she
understands the rhythmic nature of existence.
Whitmont relates she "has a sense of rhythm,
timing and a capacity for empathy. She lives,
responds to and identifies with patterns,
process and form and the needs and tides of
the body and bodily existence" (1980, p.
116).

Regarding her ability at facilitating
the dance, Hall writes, "her skill at leading
the dance is the same skill that makes her a
competent midwife. Both are based on
instinctual rhythm" (p. 112). Classic cults
invoking the Moon Goddess entailed rituals of
dancing into the wilderness, into the
darkness and returning to more conscious
civilization. It was felt that a dancer's
step could cross the boundary between life
and death. "She can teach how to make contact
with the unconscious and survive" relates
Hall (p. 112).

The Moon Goddess was also the source of
the "drawing-down and rising up energy of
plants, planters and people." This same
energy was felt to be catalyzed and expressed
in the ritual dances (Hall, p. 112). She and
her priestesses were considered shamans whose
main tools were the drumbeat and dance.

The goddess also had a dark side akin to
the moon. As this aspect she was called
Hecate and is reflective of the witch
archetype. As witch she is concerned with
effecting change on both psychic and physical
levels in individuals. Modern witches as
coven leadrs must have "the inner power and
sensitivity to channel the group's energy to
start and stop each phase of the ritual,

adjusting the timing to the mood of the circle" (Starhawk, 1979, p. 37).

All the therapists interviewed experienced the "rising-up" and "drawing-down" of energy and understood the impact and power of dance and the dance therapist as a vehicle and facilitator of an individual's capacity to enter the wilderness of the unconscious and be guided back. During the therapist's experience of the numinously intuitive, many specifically felt that they were being "guided" as well from a source that was beyond their personal existence. Two therapists in particular employed metaphores for their experiences which are unmistakeably reflective of the Mood Goddess consciousness.

Relating to the aspect of the deity as goddess of the rivers and wilderness, one dance therapist spoke of the energy source of her experience. "It's like a river that's really deep ... past ... future ... it's all the same river. There is an internal landscape. The water is dark, and very inviting, but shimmering; there's a lot of light that comes out of it ... there are fields, conifer trees ... there's no landscape architect other than creative life force."

Another dance therapist describes herself as being possessed as a witch and midwife. She writes of the group movement experence, "My own drumming increases. I feel as though I am supporting, guiding, helping give birth to this squirming monster. It is Protean, primitive archaic. We are all giving birth to it, and I am midwife. It's magic, a witch's coven, rising to an ecstatic peak. I am witch, carefully filling the rising energy, feeding and nurturing it."

313

Summary

"Matriarchal consciousness is written into a woman's body," states Eric Neumann (1973, p. 59) and so it is with the dance-movement therapist. The phenomenon of the body felt experience of the numinously intuitive is reflective of the most fundamental nature of women's mysteries and thus cannot effectively be translated into words. It is clearly more than the empirical description of the experience. These experiences go beyond the space-force-time continuum and the confines of the logic system of patriarchal Western language. But the need for the recognition of such phenomena and their impact on therapeutic process and on Western civilization as a whole is no less vital or meaningful.

Jung (1933) writes, "The body lays claim to equal recognition. If we can reconcile ourselves to the mysterious truth that the spirit is the living body seen from within, and the body the outer manifestation of the living spirit--the two being really one--then we can understand why the striving to transcend the present level of consciousness through acceptance of the unconscious must give is due to the body" (p. 253).

The dance-movement therapist is revealed here as a modern invoker-transformer of this connection to deep cyclic wisdom. She represents an important link to the past value of right brain matriarchal consciousness to a time when civilizations paid homage to the great goddesses. In the past, men and women were intitiated into her mysteries, now Western civilization attempts to understand them through analyzing the unanalyzable. The Eleusian mystery rite of Demeter-Kore-Hecate could only be understood

314

through the "dancing of it" Kerenyi relates
(1973, p. 141). The body-movement experience
provides access to both the "knowing it and
being it" phenomena (Kerenyi, 1973, p. 1982).
Only in this manner can psychic
transformation occur.

The dance-movement therapist understands
how to utilize the intuitively feminine
(right brain) body-felt experience as well as
the more patriarchal (left brain
perspective). In valuing this androgenous
orientation to being-in-the-wrod, s/he can
facilitate those in the Western culture who
are polarized into a solely linear empirical
perspective toward a richer deeper experience
of life and its mysteries.

Bibliography

Books

Adler, Margot. Drawing Down the Moon. Boston:
    Beacon Press, 1979.

Arguelles, Miriam & Arguelles, Jose. The
    Feminine-Specious as the Sky. Boulder:
    Shambhala, 1977.

Bartenieff, Irmgard. Body Movement Coping
    with the Environment. New York: Gordon &
    Breach, Science Pub., Inc., 1980.

Bernstein, Penny (Ed.) Eight Theoretical
    Approaches in Dance-Movement Therapy.
    Dubuque: Kendall-Hunt Pub., 1981.

_____. Theory and Methods in Dance-Movement
    Therapy, 3rd Edition. Dubuque: Kendall-
    Hunt Pub., 1981.

315

Binswanger, L. Being-in-the World. Jacob
Nedleman (Ed.) New York: Basic Books,
1963.

Campbell, Joseph. Myths to Live By. New York:
The Viking Press, 1972.

Castillejo, Irene Claremont De. Knowing
Woman. New York: Harper & Row Pub.,
1973.

Cirlot, J. E. A Dictionary of Symbols. New
York: Philosophical Library, 1978.

Dean, Stanley. Psychiatry and Mysticism.
Chicago: Nelson-Hall, 1979.

Eliade, Mircea. Rites and Symbols of
Initiation Mysteries of Birth and
Rebirth. New York: Harper & Row Pub.,
1975.

Giorgi, Amedeo. Psychology as a Human
Science. New York: Holt, Rinehart &
Winston, Inc., 1975.

____. Fischer William, et al. Duquesne
Studies in Phenomenological Psychology,
Vols. I & II. Pittsburgh: Duquesne
University Press, 1971, 1975.

Graves, Robert. The White Goddess. New York:
Farrar, Strauss & Giroux, 1979.

Grinnell, Robert. Alchemy in a Modern Woman.
New York: Spring Publications, 1973.

Hall, Nor. The Moon and the Virgin
Reflections on the Archetypal Feminine.
New York: Harper & Row Pub., 1980.

Harding, Esther. Psychic Energy, Its Source
and Its Transformation. Princeton:
Princeton University Press, 1963.

____. Woman's Mysteries, Ancient and Modern.
New York: Harper & Row Pub., 1971.

Jung, C. G. Memories Dreams and Reflections.
New York: Random House, 1961.

____. Symbols of Transformation. Princeton:
Princeton University Press, 1956.

____. Modern Man in Search of Soul. New York:
Harcourt, Brace & Co., 1933.

____. & Kerenyi, C. Essays on a Science of
Mythology. Princeton: Princeton
University Press, 1973.

Keen, Ernest. A Primer in Phenomenological
Psychology. New York: Holt, Rinehart &
Winston, Inc., 1975.

Kerenyi, Karl. Goddesses of Sun and Moon.
Irving: Spring Publications, Inc., 1979.

Krishna, Gopi, Kundalini the Evolutionary
Energy in Man. Boulder: Shambhala
Publications, Inc., 1971.

MacCana, Proinsias. Celtic Mythology. London:
Hamlyn Pub., 1970.

Neumann, Eric, & James Hillman, et al.
Fathers and Mothers. New York: Spring
Publications, 1973.

Ornstein, R. The Psychology of Consciousness.
New York: Viking Press, 1972.

Pomeroy, Sarah B. Goddesses, Whores, Wives,
and Slaves. New York: Schocken Books,
1975.

Sharkey, John. Celtic Mysteries. New York:
Thames and Judson, 1979.

Singer, June. Androgyny. Garden City: Anchor
Books, 1977.

Starhawk. The Spiral Dance: A Rebirth of the
Ancient Religion of the Great Goddess.
New York: Harper & Row Pub., 1979.

Stone, Merlin. Ancient Mirrors of Womanhood,
Vols. I & II. New York: New Sibylline
Books, 1979.

_____. When God Was a Woman. New York:
Harcourt Brace Jovanovich, 1976.

Tart, Charles T. States of Consciousness. New
York: E. P. Dutton Co., 1975.

Woman. Parabola Myth and the Quest for
Meaning. Vol. V., Number 4, 1980.

Zimmerman, J. E. Dictionary of Classical
Mythology. New York: Bantam Books, 1980.

Articles

Bernstein, Penny. "A Mythologic Quest:
Jungian Movement Therapy with the
Psychosomatic Client," American Journal
of Dance Therapy, Vol. III, No. 2, 1980.

Krippner, S. & Meacham, W. "Conscious and the
Creative Process," The Gifted Child
Quarterly. Autumn, 1968.

Smallwood, Joan. "Dance Therapy and the
    Transcendent Function," American Journal
    of Dance Therapy, Vol. II, No. 1, 1978.

Whitehouse, Mary Starks. "C.G. Jung and Dance
    Therapy: Two Major Principles," Eight
    Theoretical Approaches in Dance-Movement
    Therapy, Penny Bernstein, Ed. Dubuque:
    Kendall/Hunt Pub., 1979.

Whitmont, Edward C. "Reassessing Femininity
    and Masculinity: A Critique of Some
    Traditional Assumptions," Quadrant, Vol.
    13, No. 2, 1980.

Dissertations and Theses

Bernstein, Penny. Toward an Implicit Theory
    of Dance-Movement Therapy. Dissertation,
    University Microfilms, 1979.

Fay, Carolyn Grant. Movement and Fantasy: A
    Dance Therapy Model Based on the
    Psychology of Carl G. Jung. Masters
    Thesis, 1977.

Greene, Anita. The Use of Touch in Analytic
    Psychotherapy: A Case Study. Thesis ror
    N. Y. C. G. Jung Training Center, 1980.

Chapter 6

The Somatic Countertransference:
The Inner Pas de Deux

Penny Lewis Bernstein, Ph.D., ADTR

Wait without thought, for you are not
    ready for thought;
So the darkness shall be the light, and the
    stillness the dancing."

                    T.S. Eliot "East Coker"

The phenomenon of the somatic
unconscious is ever present in the embodied
bi-personal field of therapist and patient.
It is present whether the dance-movement
therapist utilizes an in depth psychotherapy
in which the phenomenon of transference-
countertranference is scrutinized or whether
s/he employs a short term adjunctive approach
to treatment. Intuitively, the dance-movement
therapist has long used his/her body as a
vessel to receive, contain, and metabolize
the patient's split off parts. Then in the
mirroring that is created, the patient's
somatic unconscious may receive an experience
of wholeness.

During the 60's, I trained with one of
the founders of dance therapy, Marian Chace.
Whle in her program at Turtle Bay with other
trainees, I recall she asked us to pair off
for an exercise. One person was to role play

321

the patient, the other, the therapist. The "patients" were asked to withdraw into a psychotic, selfless, schizophrenic state. The "therapists" were to move slowly and diagonally to sit as close as we could to our "patient's" kinesphere. We were then told to reflect the patient through external posturing, breath flow and internal somatic empathy. Our goal was "to be where they were" and in that secure, embodied symbolizing field, to assist them back into reality through gradual expressive rhythmic body action.

I remember it seemed almost magical to me at the time that it worked at all. Mostly I was grateful that it did work, particularly when Marian took us to various hospitals for field experience. She would extract her pad from her pocket and watch us like a mother hawk, jotting down notes when the impulse grabbed her. Mostly, I thought I had "guessed well" or that I had effectively "imitated" the person, or that, like some form of method acting, I had found that empty, frightened or monstrous self in me and thus knew how to enter their world. But that wasn't what was happening at all. It wasn't until many years later in my work as a therapist, as I struggled to figure ou how I could have possibly known this or that, that I began to get wise to the synchronistic presence of the somatic unconscious.

In his "The Psychology of the Transference" (C.W. vol. 16), C. G. Jung was the first psychotherapist to lay out a grid for the struggling analyst to comprehend this bi-personal process. For the purposes of this chapter, the dynamic pattern would be as depicted in figure 1.

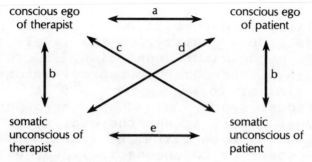

Figure 1. Transference-countertransference matrix.

Thus, not only are the patient and therapist relating to each other on a conscious level (a), in what Jung termed an "uncomplicated personal relationship", but there are other energy fields within the intra and interpersonal matrix. In (b) the therapist and patient are also effected personally by their own respective unconscious. Here the therapist's personal associations to the movement behavior of the patient can provide rich information. This phenomenon is useful as well for the patient providing there is little or no ego boundaries however, the influx from the unconscious can be overwhelming for the patient. Dance therapists have been trained to consciously pick up patient's unconscious body movment, posturing, breath flow and body tension: (c). Awareness of the fact that the patient, particularly if major psychotic or characterological conditions are present, picks up the unconscious of the therapist (d) is a phenomenon that is shortly apprehended by frequently surprised interns.

But it is to the last dynamic pattern (e) that this chapter addresses itself. This interchange of energy flow from somatic

323

unconscious to somatic unconscious is the
most subtle to perceive, but by far, the most
potentially transformative. This inner pas de
deux has a dual quality. On the level of
personal unconscious connection, it creates
an imaginal choreographic improvisational
sphere similar to Winnicott's (1971)
transitional space. On a deeper transpersonal
archetypal level, it has the quality of an
embodied vision or ritual of transformation.
This unconscious to unconscious duet exists
whether the dance therapist is talking with a
patient, silently observing the patient's
authentic movement, or dancing with the
patient. It is present from the moment s/he
enters the therapy room until the moment s/he
leaves. The capacity to receive such somatic
information described in the preceding
chapter has been identified by Schwartz
(1984) as "feminine gnosis". This inner
embodied wisdom requires a connection to an
improvisational process which on the
archetypal level results in an inner knowing
which hooks into the mundus imaginalis of an
acausal liminal dimension.

Choreographing The Inner Improvisation

    The capacity to be aware of the somatic
unconscious of the other can be facilitated
through consciously attending to the
preparatory or initial phase of the
experience of somatic synchronicity described
in the preceding chapter: a visceral emptying
which produced a vessel-like receptivity was
related along with a bodily and psychic
stillness. This stillness has a sense of
grounded weight to it. Breathing becomes
rhythmic and quiet. Tension needs to be
totally released from the soma. (Bound flow
in any part of the body is an armoring and
serves as a barrier against allowing the

patient's experience to enter the body.) For women, the uterus is imagined to be emptied to receive the split off part(s) of the individual to be reborn, whole out of her once more. In other instances a digestive/anal focus has proven to be helpful. Here the received material from the patient is digested and brought forth in its transformed state as an anal production. Anal libidinal playfulness allows for the needed subtlety of variation while the anal sadistic pole allows for the therapist to retain and "hold on to" an interpretatoin until the appropriate time (Bernstein, 1981; Schwartz, 1984).

This form of embodied knowing is antithetical to typical solar conscious reasoning which bases hypotheses on cognitive material. This is the gnosis of the darker feminine realms. Trusting that the inner container will fill with the unconscious of the other keeps the therapist grounded and embodied. It keeps him/her from the anxiety which disembodies by a manic flight upward toward the more mascline intellect. To be dumb, to say nothing, to offer no suggestions means that the patient can enter the somatic vessel and feel the safety of its groundedness and boundaries without demands or judgments. To come without an agenda translates to the patient that the therapist can be a container (Schwartz, 1984). "When you come down into your body, you help the patient be in their body" (Schwartz, 1984); and in doing so enable an inner body to inner body healing connection.

In the next phase, the dance therapists described an experience of being filled. Some related an energy coming into their body through the head or heart while others received through their vaginal canal. This energy may come from the personal split off somatic unconscious of the other, or, as the phenomena described by the dance therapists in the previous chapter, it can be of a numinous quality emerging from the archetypal unconscious or objective psyche. In either case, this energy typically can be received and perceived by the therapist through one of the four functions described by Jung (CWG).

If the sensation function is dominant in the therapist, s/he may receive the material in the form of sensate experiences such as abdominal pressure, tension, or churning. If the thinking function is the conduit, the somatic phenomena may translate into concepts such as pregnancy, inner battle, or undigestible introjects. If the therapist's feeling function is the main vehicle of this form of communication, then s/he may feel strong waves of emotion enter his/her body such as sadness, rage, longing or fear. If intuition is dominant then symbolic images and mythic themes may emerge such as in imaging of a person locked up in a castle with an ogre on guard or receiving a penetrating light from a god which allows for inner gnosis.

Whatever the experience, it has a distinct quality of "other than self", thereby giving the therapist a crucial message that it is not from his/her own countertransference reaction to the patient.

In the third phase the dance therapists have described an experience of knowing which leads to an eventual intervention, suggestion, or interpretation. Knowing what to do with this imaginal unconscious material is as crucial as the capacity to contain it. At this point it makes sense to differentiate

between the two types of phenomena: The
personal and the numinous although
in practice they need to go hand in hand.

The Somatic Transitional Space

In Winnicottian play (1971), there
exists a capacity to image an improvisation
between the therapist and patient. In this
form of reverie, a sense of dissolution can
allow the deadened off places inside the
person's body to dissolve and to be awakened
into the somatic transitional space.

What happens conceptually is that
previously the patient's split off parts have
been stored in his/her body--in the somatic
unconscious. These parts may be the bad
shadow sides of an unloved, unmirrored
infant; they may be unclaimed, embodied
sexuality or power; or they may be the
introjected psychotic parts of a
nondifferentiated merging mother. These parts
are then projected onto and into the somatic
vessel of the dance therapist. Projective
identification can be used in service to
early symbiotic needs to merge and blend with
the therapist. It can be used as a way of
gaining perspective on an affect or complex,
i.e., if the individual is possessed by
something, it is too close to delineate and
assimilate properly. This phenomenon may also
be employed as a way to be in relation to the
therapist, referred to as a desire for
linking (Grotstein, 1981). Grotstein (1981)
defines the phenomenon of projective
identification as a "mental mechanism whereby
the self experiences the unconscious fantasy
of locating itself, or aspects into an object
for exploratory or digestive purposes" (p.
123).

The countertransference can be concordant, i.e. the therapist shares the unspeakable bodily felt experience with the individual; or it can be of a complementary quality in which the therapist experiences the polarized aspect of the complex; for example, if the patient is feeling victimized, the therapist might have somatic imaginings of feeling like a rapist (Racker, 1968).

The therapist must be able to participate in this imaginal improvisation giving the patient the sense that the somatic experience has been rceived and that it can be contained. These received sensatoins or feelings may need to be stored until the resistances to the individual's integration of the material be explored both bodily and imaginally and brought to conscious awareness for consideration. Maladaptive breath flow (Bernstein, 1981), body tension and splitting, pockets of chronic pain, and other psychosomatically based systemic responses such as circulatory, digestive and elimination disorders may need to be addressed (Elkin, 1971).

If the therapist feels compelled to interpret or reflect back the somatic experience, a red flag should be waved. Frequently, this is just the time to save the impulse and let the material digest more. The time to verbalize emerges when the inner sensations are quieted, calmed so that they may be better taken in by the patient. Regurgitate the material too quickly and the paient will have the feeling that the therapist cannot contain their somatic projection (Schwartz, 1984). This may take time. With schizoid splitting, there may be so many fragmented pieces inside the therapist from the patient that, like with a

1000 piece puzzle, laborious, meditative sorting and concentration is needed. In other instances, as with borderline individuals, the therapist may feel flooded with the patient's rage or filled with their grandiose inflation. With borderlines in particular, it is vital to offer both sides of the projection as reflection or interpretation so that their potential wholeness is mirrored (Schwartz, 1984).

Clinical Grounding

With one borderline woman, I described the choreography of her feelings toward me, "I feel one part of you wants to crawl into my lap while another part of you wants to shove me far away." She responds, "Yes, part of me wants to come over to you. You look like such a comfortable bed, but the rest of me wants to scratch your eyes out."

With many patients, I am filled with their negative, introjected mother which gets somatically projected into me for the purpose of detoxification and transformation. With one woman I began feeling overfilled with hysterical anxiety like so many frenetic mice racing through my stomach and intestines. I felt like I was being driven crazy. After calming these inner mice, I respond, "I feel like you were filling me with your mother's overflowing hysteria in hopes that I could contain it and calm her craziness in you." At that point, she left her manic flight, and I felt her reenter her body as she breathed slowly and deeply into her pelvis, experiencing it as a calm, safe vessel.

A schizoidal woman lies down on the floor in an active imagination body movement experience. She doesn't move. I begin feeling

329

a powerful, envious, menacing witch enter me.
I imaged she/me invading her space and
disrupting her process. Then I feel the
experience disappear, and I have an emptied
clarity. When she arises, she describes
reexperiencing a dream she had had the night
before in which she had placed a vessel in an
altar in her room. Her mother entered the
room and moved about asking her where the
vessel had come from, yelling at her, "Did
you put it there?" She responds, "It's my
room and my cup, and I have a perfect right
to put it there."

In the next session, as she lay down to
be in her body, I again had this powerful
feeling of being a witch-like negative female
force who wanted to cut her in two at the
waist and take her pelvis to possess it. When
she sits up, she reports that she hadn't made
love with her lover since she had told her
mother that she had moved in with him. Her
mother was horrified, "You're a tramp! What
about me! I'm home with your father doing the
dishes." After this, she goes back into
authentic movement and rips off pieces of a
symbolic chastity belt in which her witch-
like mother complex had locked her sexuality.

With others it is the negative
father complex with which I become filled.
When one woman begins her authentic movement
experience, I commence the process of
emptying myself and become filled almost
immediately with a cold, sadistic judge that
devalues her embodied feminine experience.
From this it became clear why it was so
difficult and impossible at times for her to
move in my presence.

Parental complexes are not the only
psychic constellations to be projected onto
the therapist. Stein (1984) discusses the

phenomena of power complex projection in depth. Some examples can be found in suggesting a technique, giving unsolicited advice, talking a great deal, and literally taking up more space in the room.

A movement analytic patient who is working toward reclaiming her embodied feminine power deiminishes her voice and retreats. I feel a strong surge of power and feel as if I am 1∅ feet tall looming over her. I have to keep myself from speaking in a loud voice. I respond that she has given me all her power and she leaves only the victim stance for herself. She explores moving from a powerful to enfeelbed posture finding a middle, modal place somatically and psychically.

The somatic countertransference may be of a concordant nature as with another woman who lay down on my studio carpet beginning an active imagination movement process. I became aware that I was not just going through my usual embodied quieting, but that I felt a compelling pressure to have to be still, and to breathe as little as possible. Afterward, the patient reported an image of her father entering the room. His presence felt like a crushing weight on her chest curtailing her breathing. She would do her best to diminish her presence in a room when he would enter it as a child lest his massive rage find her as a target.

Mostly, however, it is the wounded split off infant self of the patient that I hold in my uterus. A borderline man is talking in a flat, two dimensional manner. I begin feeling and imagining an angry, screaming, wounded child inside of me that feels not part of my psychology. I reflect that I hear the part of him that is adult and in control and I also feel the rageful, wounded child inside of him that longs to be heard and cared for. It was at that point that he could say, "before I felt we were in two separate bubbles--now I feel like we are in the same space. It's frightening to me, but I know I need to be here with you."

This experience can last for months just as it does in the natural gestation process. This was the case for a woman (Bernstein, 1982) who had been unseen, unattended to and unreflected by a cold, rejecting mother. When her infant self had come to term, she began having dreams of the transformation of her mother complex and the joint birthing of her healed infant self.

On other occasions, the somatic unconscious dance is one of shared emotion. A man entered my office like a tightly contained bomb. As he spoke, I became filled with waves of longing and sadness swirling with currents of rage. Reflecting this to him at the appropriate time enabled him to begin to have his feelings for himself toward his own self valuing.

Another man with a strong mother complex and puer attitude continuously brought in many elaborate dreams and would resist the relationship and his own inner descent through their Appollonian reflection and "high flying puer" analysis. Through mutual embodiment of a dream symbol, I began feeling a deep rush of burning, painful anguish course upward from my belly to my heart. I reflected this back to him. He was profoundly moved and said that he had never before felt so deeply known.

These affect charged somatic links can serve to draw upon whole memories of childhood and infancy that need to be remembered and reexperienced. My silence brings a flood of negative projections from a woman whose mother cut her of from the love that was her birth right to have. I meanwhile feel a queasy, churning, butterfly-like sensation in my stomach. When I report this, she connects to a hospital experience in early childhood in which her mother, without explanation, abandoned her to have her stomach pumped. She recalls thinking in utter terror that her mother was having her killed.

The Embodied Self and the Dance of the Numinous

No matter what phenomenon fills the somatic vessel, a connection to the Self is vital. Without the therapist's relationship to that which has the capacity to heal, to draw the polarized parts of the patient together, the work has an absence of depth, of soul, of embodied spirit. Without a relationship to the transpersonal wellspring, both the therapist and patient are ripped off. Therapists who reduce idealizing archetypal projections to a personal level are in real danger. They may be caught in archetypal inflation just as Icarus discovered when he flew too close to the power of the sun and today's political leaders who feel they have the power to decide the potential destruction of the earth and its inhabitants. For the patient this is a psychic rape. Schwartz (1984) feels that borderline individuals in particular have denied their connection to the numinous out of parental envy and need to reclaim their visionary capacity.

Being in an embodied relation to the Self means staying connected to a powerfully calm experience of inner wholeness. This deepens and enriches the personal experience of the inner container with the transformative power of the archetype. The somatic vessel then becomes what was described in Chapter 5 as the inner grail, the communion cup of the Self, the wellspring at Eleusius, the vase of Isis and the womb of the Earth mother.

Embodiment is vital as the spiritual realm can send the unsuspecting therapist out of the room and into the "heavens". This is just as disabling as having unconsciously blocked or reduced all connection to the Self to the human realm. Embodying the Self incarnates the spirit realm. This is the theme of the ancient Eleusinian rites, Christian communion, and Kundalini yoga, and requires a grounded centered body or visceral temenos.

Embodying the Self also means embodying the mythic transformation rite that needs to occur in the individual's individuation process. This form of knowing and healing has existed for 20-30 thousand years in the shamanistic traditions of Africa, native North and South America, Australia, Sibera, Central Asia and northern Europe. It is a phenomenal pocess by which the shaman or healer enters an altered state of consciousness, receives the dis-ease whether it be physical or psychic from the patient into his or her body; and then restores the individual's natural power or lost soul.

It was this journey of initiation into shamanism which manifested itself as the personal myth of a woman who began to claim her power as a healer. While I sat emptied and still, I felt a powerful, numinous energy

334

enter me. She reported seeing all women of all ages and cultures passed through me.

In another session she embodied the feline cat aspect of her feminine nature with such fullness that I felt there was a cat in the room and I had to keep my own cat which was awakened in me from moving with her. In the following session she again constellated the numinous. The power in the room was thick. "Oh, Penny!" she exclaimed, her eyes quite wide. "You became a hugh leopard."

It was not until I reread on shaminism that it became clear, that the leopard was her power animal which is, initally, evoked through its embodiment (Harner, 1982; Andrews, 1981).

In a subsequent session, she again embodies her cat. She moves to the floor and claws at the rug/ground. I, meanwhile, sitting still to maintain my somatic container, feel a peaceful, wise, old woman presence enter me. "I am well pleased with you," is the phrase which emerges from this imaginal archetype. She reports digging for something; and before she could continue, this old voice says within me, "She has found the crystal." My patient continues to say she has found a clear stone. Then she stills herself and reports seeing two of me: one, my usual self; the other, larger older, and very wise.

At other times the numinous emerges in the form of a conunctio or mystical union between patient and analyst. Here there is a mutuality of shared experience. Much has been written about this process between the male analyst and female patient. But this experence is not limited to this pairing. Such was the case with a female patient with

whom I was in the process of terminating. She
had reported a dream in which she embodied
her masculine and creative feminine sides
(her personal version of the emerging birth of
the hermaphroditic self) a deep silence
filled the room. She looked out the large
window behind my left shoulder and mentioned
the wind which was gently but powerfully
making its presence known. The wind,
frequently employed as a religious symbol of
the breath of the spirit of life of the
Godhead, seemed to enter the room. Jung (CW,
vol. 16) writes of the return of the soul
during the alchemical process in the
"Psychology of the Transference," "Here the
reconciler, the soul, dives down from heaven
to breathe life into the dead body" (p. 283).
(See figure 2 of the Rosarium Philosophorum

PHILOSOPHORVM

ANIMÆ IVBILATIO SEV
Ortus feu Sublimatio.

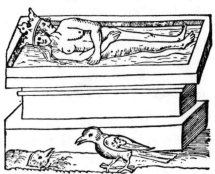

Die fchwingt fich die fele hernidder/
Vnd erquickt den gereinigten leychnam wider-

Figure 2. The Reembodiment of the soul/
spirit. (From the Alchemical series: Rosarium
Philosophorum, C.G. Jung, CW16, p. 285).

series). For women this soul has a masculine quaity which seeks to "discern and discriminate" (p. 204).

I felt a compelling energy to maintain visual connection to her. She slowly moves her eyes from the outside to my eyes. Our eyes, like some awesome energy conduit, remained fixed. I felt my body seemingly disappear; it was as if my eyes were given over in service to an all powerful objective psyche and I was seeing through the experience of the Self. My eyes now rivetted, I began to see a wavy flow of energy over her head. While it stayed over her, the room filled with a blinding light. When it returned to normal, I saw this energy enter into her body. In stillness, she then remarks, "There was more than just you and me in this room." I nod my head. She continues, "I felt like I or something was hovering over me almost like an out of body experience. I feel very full and peaceful." I meanwhile could experience a lighted space between each cell, each atom of my body. I felt very clear.

Jung (CW 16) writes regarding the differences between masculine and feminine in the reanimation of the body, "The man's opus is concerned with the erotic aspect of the anima, while the woman's is concerned with the animus which is a "function of the head" (p. 303).

Schwartz's (1984a) discussion of the "self that hovers" in the liminal nature of a coniunctio experience, I believe, also pertains here. He writes, "This brings a sense of mutual respect, equality, and concern on a very deep level, as if blood had been exchanged. The term often used for this experience is communitas. Communitas implies not only the structure of communion or community but also a kind of "substance," as though it could be transmitted; it is neither

337

a purely physical nor purely psychic reality
but a paradoxical combination of them"
(p.11).

Thus both the therapist and patient join
in the transformative experience which seeks
to embody or reincarnate soul/spirit. This
numinous communitas experience has been
coined from the work of Turner (1974) on
ritual process, who speaks of its power in
group ritual dance experiences. Here the
group gestalt is the patient or "other"
typically moving synchronously in repetitive
rhythmic body action. The numinous has been
experienced to fill the somatic vessel of the
dance therapist who is guided by the Self in
one of its manifestations toward inner gnosis
of archetypal movements and ancient rites of
passage. Here again the universal and
transpersonal has been received by the
somatic container of the therapist.

Detoxifying and Clearing
the Somatic Container

Maintaining an uncontaminated somatic
vessel is vital in patients' experience that
their unique depth can be held by the
therapist. Personal material seepage can be
monitored by good supervision and personal
depth movement therapy. Toxicity, accumulated
in the therapist's body from the
psychosomatic matrix of patients occurs
typically when the therapist is unconscious
of his/her own corresponding or compensatory
complex. These lacunae or holes in awareness
need to be explored with the same integrity
and humility in relation to inner gnosis as
the patients' material is regarded. As soon
as the therapist becomes aware of potential
somatic toxicity, the sensate, body felt
experience needs to be explored in an inner,
silent dance. If still in session with the

338

patient, an imaginal, authentic movement exploration can be undertaken to retrieve a connection to one's personal myth and its relation to that of the patient's. If out of session, this can take a more active embodied form.

A graduate student complained of tension in her neck on a break in one of my classes. I lengthened her spine and aligned her head. A feeling charged somatic memory that had previously been cut off had been called up during a class exercise and was blocked from conscious expression. Once aligned, she began to have the needed remembering. When the class resumed and I began talking, I found I had an acute case of laryngitis. I had not cleared myself and the somatic countertransference had lodged in the corresponding area in my body. As soon as I could, I began addressing its meaning and my own unconsciousness. What affect in me, what childhood memory needed to be found and like a homeless orphan be reclaimed and consciously acknowledged.

Giving meaning to somatic vestiges of patients' process transforms the somatic reaction in the therapist just as it does with the patient. "What is this body sensation saying to me?" "What does this pain, tension, emotion want?" "What is my body clamouring to bring into consciousness?" "What part of my inner myth is this reflective of?" are some of the questions which can link the therapist to meaning and personal centroversion or individuation.

Conclusion

The inner pas de deux of the somatic countertransference is the bipersonal vessel

of transformation. It links the deepest core
of the patient to the healing container of the
therapist. Here, in this secure field, wounds
are acknowledged, negative introjects are
detoxified and transformed, split off pieces
are found and drawn together in wholeness,
and the instinctual body is reanimated with
soul/spirit in an emotional connection to the
Self.

Bibliography

Andrews, Lynn. Medicine Woman. San
Francisco: Harper & Row, 1981.

Bernstein, Penny and Singer, David, Eds. The
Choreography of Object Relations. Keene:
Antioch University-New England Pub.,
1982.

_____. Ed. Eight theoretical Approaches in
Dance-Movement Therapy. Dubuque:
Kendall/Hunt Pub., 1979.

_____. Theory and Methods in Dance-Movement
Therapy, Third Ed. Dubuque: Kendall/Hunt
Pub., 1981.

Eigen, Michael. "The Area of Faith in
Winnicott, Lacan, and Bion". In
International Journal of Psycho
Analysis. 62,413,1981.

Eliade, Mircea. Shamanism Archaic Techniques
of Ecstasy. Princeton: Princeton
University Press, 1974.

Elkin, Henry. "On Selfhood and the
Development of Ego Structures in
Infancy". In The Psychoanalytic
Quarterly, 1971.

Fordham, Michael. "Technique and
     Countertranference". In Technique in
     Jungian Analysis by Michael Fordham.
     London: Wm. Heinemann Medical Books,
     1974.

Gordon, Rosemary. "The Concept of Projective
     Identification". In The Journal of
     Analytic Psychology. London: Tavistock
     Publications, 1965.

Grotstein, James. Splitting and Projective
     Identification. New York: Jason Aronson,
     1981.

Harner, Michael. The Way of the Shaman. New
     York: Bantam Books, 1982.

Jung, C. G. The Practice of Psychotherapy CW
     Vol. 16, Princeton: Princeton University
     Press, 1977.

_____. Psychological Types CW Vol. 16.
     Princeton: Princeton University Press,
     1977.

Racker, Heinrich. Transference and
     Countertransference. New York:
     International Universities Press, 1982.

Schwartz-Salant, Nathan. "Archetypal Factors
     Underlying Sexual Acting-out in the
     Transference/countertransference
     Process". In Chiron, Wilmette: Chrion
     Pub., 1984a.

_____. and Stein, Murray, Ed. Chiron:
     Transference/Countertransference.
     Wilmette: Chiron Pub., 1984.

_____. Narcissism and Character
     Transformation. Toronto: Inner City
     Books, 1982.

341

_____. "Transference and Countertransference."
New York: C. G. Jung Institute of New
York, course, Oct., 1983-May 1984.

Searles, Harold. Countertransference and
Related Subjects. New York:
International Universities Press, 1981.

Stein, Murray. "Power, Shamanism, and
Maieutics in the Counter-Tranference."
In Chiron, Wilmette: Chiron Pub., 1984.

Stevens, Barbara. "A Critical Assessment of
the work of Robert Langs". In Library
Journal, San Francisco C.G. Jung
Institute, 1982.

Turner, Victor. The Ritual Process. Chicago:
Aldine Pub. Co., 1969.

Winnicott, D. W. Playing and Reality. New
York: Penguin Books, 1971.

Appendix

Expressive Arts Assessment Profile in Jungian, Object Relations and Psychodynamic Therapy

Penny Lewis Bernstein Ph.D., ADTR

General Information

1. Name   2. Age   3. Date

4. Socioeconomic, ethnic, religious background

5. Under what circumstances were observations gathered

6. Family of origin

   Mother

   Father

   Siblings and their order

   Significant others in family

7. Present status

   e.g., Married, children, work, hospitalization

   Significant relationship(s)

8. Reason for referral and presenting problems

9. History

10. Dominant complexes

    a. Ego functioning and major defenses

    b. Mother

    c. Father

    d. Animus/a

    e. Persona

    f. Shadow

    g. Other

11. Major resistances employed

12. Transference/countertransference issues

13. Major archetypal themes

Autism
1. Fixated at autistic stage
2. No initial capacity for object relationship
3. No transference possible
4. Archetypal investment in objects

Psychosis
1. Fixated at symbiotic stage
2. Little or no ego
3. Archetypal merger in uroboric stage of post-natal embryonic phase

Character Disorder
Narcissism
1. Fixated at symbiotic stage
2. Has some level of ego functioning
3. Inflated with the archetypal
4. Expects mirroring transference
5. Grandiosity reinforced: only good self and object tolerance

Borderline
1. Fixated at the rapproachment phase of separation and individuation
2. Has some ego functioning
3. Split good/bad self and object
4. Archetypal is projected onto therapist in idealized transference

Neurosis
1. Has obtained object constancy
2. Internalized integrated whole self and object representations
3. Has working ego
4. Capacity for heroic and heroinic quest
5. Capacity for appropriate ego-Self axis

MAJOR DEVELOPMENTALLY HOUSED
DIAGNOSTIC CATEGORIES

(along with associated
Countertransference Reactions)

	Dominant	Present Only in Stress
I. Autism--Fixated at autistic stage uroboric-pleromatic stage		
1. Bizarre movement		
2. Interpersonal movement relations which indicate deanimation of object		
3. Therapist not used as symbiotic body ego buffer		
4. Movement which indicates lack of differentiation among animate and inanimate objects		
5. Little or no shape flow		
6. Derailed and fragmented oral and phallic tension flow rhythms		
7. Fragmentation produced by dysynchronized tension flow rhythms		
8. Peripheral bound flow		
9. Complementary somatic countertransference reaction of feeling deanimated and depersonalized		
II. Psychosis--Fixated at symbiotic stage postnatal embryonic phase		
1. Body merges with that of therapist		
2. Somatic counter-transference reaction of		

348

	Dominant	Present Only in Stress
feeling blended and merged with patient		
3. Predominance of neutral flow		
4. Predominance of oral rhythms		
5. Diffusion of effort flow phrasing		
6. Run-on body movement sequences		
7. Fixed narrowed, sunken and/or hollowed body shape flow		
8. Absence of efforts--no ego adaptation to reality		
9. Absence of shaping--no ego involvement in object relations		
10. Flooded with the archetypal--giving the experience of being personally uninhabited		

III. Character Disorder

A. Narcissistic Character Disorder-- Fixated at symbiotic stage post-natal embryonic phase

	Dominant	Present Only in Stress
1. Body merges with that of therapist but has sufficient ego to monitor it		
2. Somatic counter-transference reaction of feeling blended or merged at times with patient		
3. Expansive body shaping		
4. Complementary somatic countertransference reaction of being		

349

	Dominant	Present Only in Stress

squished, flattened or
diminished
5. Complementary somatic
countertransference
internal reaction of
being overstuffed with
patient's inflation
6. Full unindividuated shape
signature that adapts to
receive narcissistic
supplies
7. Concordant somatic
countertransference
reaction of emptiness.

B.   Borderline Character
Disorder--
Fixated at
the rapproachment phase
second matriarchal stage
1. Tense (bound flow) body
periphery used for
somatic differentiation
and as defense against
engulfment
2. Complementary somatic
countertransference of
feeling filled with
idealization OR
3. Complementary somatic
countertransference of
feeling bad, cold and
withholding
4. Concordant somatic
countertransference of
feeling empty, hopeless,
helpless
5. Concordant somatic
countertransference of
feeling full of rage
6. Diminished shaping (lack
of adaptation to object
world)

	Dominant	Present Only in Stress
7. Lack of posture-gesture merger		
8. Diminished efforts (lack of ego adaptation)		

IV. Neurotic--Obtained object constancy
Chthonian stage fixation
(after 6)

1. Dominance of inner genital rhythm
2. Dominance of outer genital/phallic rhythms
3. Presence of chthonic symbols such as creatures of death, of the night, sea, or underground
4. Presence of themes of being in life threatening positions with beasts or monsters
5. Complementary somatic countertransference of being a witch or other dark, feminine character

V. Neurotic--Magic warlike stage fixation
Magical creative stage fixation (after 18)

1. Male/animus--dominance of themes of killing the dragon mother complex
2. Male/animus--limited to interest in sportslike movements and themes
3. Female/anima--dominance of themes of being rescued from a beast who needs to be transformed

351

	Dominant	Present Only in Stress
4. Female/anima--limited to themes of chaos, spaciness and a simple relationship to nature		
5. Complementary somatic countertransference of a feeling of being killed by or rescuing the patient		
VI. <u>Neurotic--Solar</u> warlike <u>phase</u> fixation <u>Lunar</u> cyclic phase fixation (after 25)		
1. Male/animus--dominance of rational, intellectualizing; inability to embody experience		
2. Concordant somatic countertransference of feeling in the head, cut off from the body		
3. Complementary somatic countertransference of feeling a soulful, embodied connection to the feminine, a sense of grounded connection to the earth, feelings and relatedness		
4. Male/animus--loss of connection to the internal, cyclic, and instinctual soma		
5. Female/anima--themes of being drawn into the darker realms of the feminine		
6. Concordant somatic countertransference of feeling lost in chaos, loss of conscious clarity		

	Dominant	Present Only in Stress

about process, feeling
dizzy, tired
7. Complementary somatic
countertransference
similar to #2

VII. <u>Neurotic--Heroic</u> <u>quest</u>
<u>fixation</u>
<u>Heroinic</u> <u>quest</u> <u>fixation</u>
(after 45)
1. Male/animus--solar
rational fixation, use of
secondary
personalization: the
experience of the
numinous, and archetypal
themes and symbols are
reduced to mundane and
personally subjective
experiences
2. Concordant somatic
countertransference of
feeling cut off from
one's connection to the
Self
3. Female/anima--caught in
the feminine through
overvaluing the embodied,
intuitive, expressive
art experience to the
exclusion of a rational,
verbal connection and
analytic thinking
4. Hieros gamos themes of
the masculine and
feminine joining through
sexual or other forms of
union
5. Somatic counter-
transference of erotic
energy
6. Anima possession in men--
expressive themes of

	Dominant	Present Only in Stress
depression and moodiness; lack of fighting efforts		
7. Concordant somatic countertransference of feeling heavy, dead, pulled into a dark, hopeless abyss or web or of being cursed		
8. Complementary somatic countertransference of feeling light with a desire to connect or rescue		
9. Animus possession in women--movement patterns which are angular, saggital, directional; lack of indulging efforts		
10. Concordant somatic countertransference of feeling strongly aggressive, ready to strike out, or of being coldly analytical		
11. Complementary somatic countertransference of feeling soft, earthy, receptive, power grounded in the earth		
12. Advanced heroic quest-- themes of descent, death, mutiliation, and/or dismemberment		
13. Advanced heroinic quest: paternal uroboros-- embodied themes of being powerfully penetrated by the archetypal masculine		
14. Somatic counter-transference of the experience of the numinous		

354

	Dominant	Present Only in Stress
VIII. <u>On the way toward</u> <u>individuation</u>		
1. Themes of resurrection and rebirth		
2. Embodied ego-Self axis		
3. Somatic counter-transference of the experience of the Self in the other and of a Self to Self alliance i.e. an "I-Thou" relationship		

Earth Mother, 300, 306-310, 314-315, 334
Edinger, E., 101, 103, 122, 123, 138, 142-143
Efforts, 80, 353-354
Effort-shape, 77, 79-83, 86, 353-354
Ego complex, 122-123, 346, 347
Egg (philosophers' egg), 152, figure 17
Ego psychology, 74, 83
Ego-Self axis, 123, 152, 347, 355
Elephant, 124
Eleusian mystery rites, 111, 145-146, 308,
        314, 334
Eliade, M., 308
Eliot, T. S., 321
Elkin, 328
Emptiness, 73, 350
Enactive cognition, 70
Enactive mode, 265, 269
Enactment, 34-35, 40, 42, 51, 60
Enmeshed families, 205-206
Erikson, E., 68, 103, 262
Experiencing, 267-269
Eyes, 147

Facilitating environment, 74
Fairbairn, R., 67, 72, 83, 85-86, 261
False self, 117
Family choreography, 223
Family dance, 220
Family freeze, 222
Family in therapy, 195-196
    Evolutionary, 196-197; Dysfunctional,
        197-199
Family sculpting, 223
Father archetype, 109, 113, 128
Father complex, 105 150, 346, 354
Fay, C., 302
Feet, 29-30, 54
Feminine gnosis, 324
FIRO, 188, 200, 202-204
Ford, 203
Fordham, M., 67, 102, 103, 105
Free flow, 77
Freud, A., 68, 77

Freud, S., 263, 266
Functional technique, 14-17

Ge, 307
Geis, 118
Gendlin, E., 258, 267-268
Genital rhythm, 79, 104
Giorgi, A., 300
Glands, 5
Goddess Archetype, 295, 300-315
Gold, 142-144
Golden Ass, 307
Grail, 309, 334
Grail quest, figure 12, 139-136
Grandmother, 130
Grasping, 8
Greene, A., 297
Greenson, R., 70
Grotstein, 327
Growing shape flow, 78, 83
Guntrip, H., 67, 71, 85, 88

Haley, J., 209, 217
Hall, N., 110, 295, 297, 307, 308, 310, 312
Handling, 75, 80, 88, 124
Hands, 27, 30, 32, 39, 43
Harding, 110, 295, 297, 308, 309, 312
Harner, 335
Hawkins, A., 259
Heart, 130
Hecate, 312, 313-314
Hemisphere; left, 299, 300; right, 299, 300,
        301
Hera, 307
Hermaphrodite, figure, 19, 336
Hero, 108, 117, 132-140, 347, 353-354
Heroine, 108, 132-140, 152, 347, 353-354
Hieros gamos, figure 14, 108, 117, 142, 158,
        353
Hillman, J., 295, 297, 310
Hoffman, 204, 210
Holding, 75, 80, 86, 87, 88, 121, 154, 159-
        160, 277

361

Holding environment, 86-87, 99, 126, 149, 278
Horowitz, 264
Horse, 124

Icarus, 333
ICO Open Score, 239
Idealized transference, 89, 347, 350
Identified patient, 196, 208, 237
Image mode, 265
Improvisation, 4, 40
Inaction, 13
Incest, 105
Inclusion, 200
Individuation, 100, 355
Inflation, 101, 350
Isaac, 161
Ishtar, 307
Isis, 100, 307, 309, 334

Jacobson, 261
Jonah (and the whale), 105
Jung, C. G., 100, 119, 152, 155, 156, 158, 161,
        162, 314 322-323, 336, 337

Kali, 114
Kerenyi, 315
Kernberg, O., 82-83
Kestenberg, J., 77, 79, 86-87, 88-89, 93, 207,
        261
Kinesphere, 202, 210
Kinesthetic empathy, 277, 278, 322
Kinesthetic images, 271, 274-275
Kinetic images, 271, 280
Kinetic translations, 238, 243
Klein, M., 75-76
Kohut, H., 67, 72, 73, 74, 75, 76, 82, 83, 85,
        89, 90
Krippner, S., 302
Krishna, 310
Kundalini, 116, 139, 158, 309, 334

Laban, 77, 210, 302
Lacunae, 338

362

Laing, R., 259, 277
Lamb, W., 210
Lexical mode, 265, 269
Life force, 18
Linking, 327
Lotus, 124
Luke, H., 165, 297
Lunar cyclic phase, 107-108, 131-132, 352-353
Lunar intuitive phase, 108

Magic warlike stage, 104, 128-130, 351-352
Magical creative stage, 104-105, 128-130,
        351-352
Mahler, M., 65, 67, 71-74, 76, 82, 83-84, 101-
        102, 126, 161
Mandala, 124
Marriage, 132
Masks, 119-120, 130
Maslow, 108, 268
Matriarchal archetypal view, 299, 314
Matriarchal consciousness, 265, 300, 314
Matriarchal phases, 101, 103, 126-127, 149,
        347-351
Medium, 300, 310-311
Medusa, 115
Meissner, 95
Mercury, 142, 152, 164
Mermaid, 128, 129
Merton, 262
Midwife, 311
Milling, 222
Minuchin, S., 194, 211
Mirroring (transference), 89-91, 121, 126,
        154, 347, 349
Monster, 102, 122, 351
Moon goddess, 300, 311-313
Mortificatio, 143, 144
Mother archetype, 101, 104, 128, 131, 164
Mother complex, 114, 149-150, 346, 351

Namma, 307
Narcissism, 69, 347, 349-350
Negredo stage, 142